FRANKOMA

And Other Oklahoma Potteries

with Price Guide

Phyllis and Tom Bess

Schiffer Publishing Ltd

77 Lower Valley Road, Atglen, PA 19310

WE LOVINGLY DEDICATE
THIS BOOK TO OUR LORD JESUS CHRIST
OUR SOON COMING KING

"He (Jesus) isn't really being slow about His promised return, even though it sometimes seems that way. But He is waiting, for the good reason that He is not willing that any should perish, and He is giving more time for sinners to repent." II Peter 3:9 *The Living Bible*

ABBREVIATIONS USED THROUGHOUT THE BOOK

I	Introduced
D	Discontinued
H	Height
L	Length
W	Width
No.	Mold Number
SA	Still Available
Diam	Diameter
Mk	Mark

Published by Schiffer Publishing, Ltd.
77 Lower Valley Road
Atglen, PA 19310
Please write for a free catalog.
This book may be purchased from the publisher.
Please include $2.95 postage.
Try your bookstore first.

We are interested in hearing from authors with book ideas on related subjects.

Printed in Hong Kong.
ISBN: 0-88740-740-4

Library of Congress Cataloging-in-Publication Data

Bess, Phyllis.
    Frankoma and other Oklahoma potteries/by Phyllis and Tom Bess.
        p.   cm.
    Includes bibliographical references and index.
    ISBN 0-88740-740-4
    1. Frankoma Pottery Company. 2. Pottery--20th century--Oklahoma. 3. Ceramic sculpture--20th century--Oklahoma. I. Bess, Tom. II. Title
NK4210.F623B39
738'.09766'075--dc20   94-46709
                                         CIP

ACKNOWLEDGMENTS

We first want to thank these gracious and wonderful ladies who have been so kind and generous with their time, pottery, catalogs, newspaper clippings, photographs and most of all, their friendship. They have given us so much of themselves and there are no words to express our love and appreciation for them. To them, we say Thank You! God bless each one of you, abundantly.

Joniece, Grace Lee and
  Donna Frank - Frankoma Pottery
Marjorie Tate - Tamac Pottery
Flora Hammat - Hammat Originals
Clara Arter - Winart Pottery
Elizabeth Synar Cramer - Synar Ceramics

Others who have helped in numerous ways, we thank you:

Nate Anderson	Howard Plunkett
Ken Coughman	Terry Randall
Bob Daniels	Chea Redditt
Dick Danielson	Maxine Sadler
Bob Hase	Gary Schaum
Bill & Suzie Holloway	Robert Stubbs
Paul Isbell	Vickie Surry
Jim & Gloria Jordan	Joseph R. Taylor
Linda Kasmarcik	Diana & Joe Walton
Mariann & Darryl Kirk	June & Dean Weimer
Tom Lottinville	

Pictured on cover:

Frankoma Dealer Sign
Frankoma Cowboy
Winart "Miami" Ashtray
Sequoyah Vase
Hammat Originals Flower Bowl

Contents

Hammat Originals
CHRISTMAS TREE TRAY
15 1/2"

Introduction

The idea of this book was birthed in 1983. We had just published our first book "Frankoma Treasures" and, while at a showing of that book, a friend asked "Why don't you do a book on (manufactured) Oklahoma pottery?" We knew, to the collector, that such a book was desired and in time would be needed. For we had seen many interesting and desirable pieces of pottery with unusual stickers or marks, all indicating that they were made in Oklahoma. No one seemed to know much about them, as we heard many conflicting stories. Anyway, the seed had been planted, and with the help of our Lord, Jesus Christ, it came into fruition.

We had always felt that we would write another book about Frankoma, and to that end we continued to collect and photograph those rare and unusual pieces that were not shown in our first book. Recent changes in management and products also require updating.

Through the years, we have not only seen a remarkable increase of interest in Frankoma, but in all the other Oklahoma potteries as well. The rising fad of fifties collectables has made some of these, such as "Tamac," eagerly sought after by those desiring the flair of those golden years.

The interest in American Indian culture and artifacts is greater than it has ever been. More and more collectors are on the hunt for Indian pottery, "Sequoyah" pottery being one of the most desirable.

With all this said, we came to the point, over a year ago, that we could take care of both projects by combining them into a single book. There were a few other pottery businesses we would have liked to cover for you, but the passing of people and poor record keeping have made it almost impossible. Maybe later! But, what we have learned we are happy to share in hopes of helping you, the collector, discover some of the best Oklahoma offers in collectable ceramic art.

FRANKOMA
MOTHER BIRD   H-3 1/2"   No. 108
BABY BIRD   H-3 1/2"   No. 109
I-1977-SA   Glaze-Bone
Designed by Grace Lee Frank Smith

Frankoma Pottery
Sapulpa, Oklahoma
1933-Present

John Nathaniel Frank was born January 31, 1905 in the slums of Chicago, Illinois. All through his school years he excelled in art. At the age of nineteen he entered The Art Institute of Chicago and began his formal education. He was there three years. He also studied at Alfred University in New York.

In the spring of 1927, Dr. Oscar B. Jacobson, with the University of Oklahoma, contacted The Art Institute of Chicago, looking for someone to establish a new ceramic art department at the University. John Frank, being an outstanding student and an assistant to one of the professors, was highly recommended. He was chosen for this new position and moved to Norman, Oklahoma, site of the University, in August of 1927. He built and furnished the Ceramic Art Department in what was once the Armory Building; thus began his teaching career.

Grace Lee Bowman was born on September 4, 1905, in a small western Oklahoma town called Orlando. After graduating from high school in Waurika, Oklahoma, she attended business college. While working for the Oklahoma Cotton Grower's Association in Oklahoma City, she met John Frank and seven months later they were married. They moved to Norman, near the University.

In 1933, John Frank purchased a partially burnt building in Norman and repaired it enough to keep out the rain. There he and Grace Lee began producing pottery. They had one kiln, a butter churn for mixing clay, fruit jars for grinding glazes and a few other crude tools. They named their new business, "FRANK POTTERIES".

John Frank continued teaching at the University. He and Grace Lee worked evenings and weekends making pottery for their new business. John resigned from the University in 1936 to devote his full attention to producing utility art pottery, pieces that were useful as well as artistic.

Their pottery was peddled around Norman to different businesses, but only a few ventured to buy anything for resale, as most were reluctant because of the unquestionable depression market for pottery. As a result, the pottery was not very profitable and there was no money for advertising. The Franks felt a name change might help boost sales. Being the only commercial pottery in the state, they borrowed the last three letters of Oklahoma and named their little company "FRANKOMA POTTERIES."

In spite of their dedication, the name change and all the hard work, their business was not prospering. They decided to relocate and chose Sapulpa, a small town approximately fifteen miles southwest of Tulsa, to build Frankoma's new plant.

By this time John and Grace Lee had two daughters, Donna Ruth, born March 24, 1932 and Joniece, born January 11, 1938. Both girls were to follow creative pursuits, Donna in writing and Joniece in ceramics.

In February of 1938, the Franks moved to Sapulpa and construction began on a small factory just north of the Sapulpa city limits on Highway 66 (years later renamed Frankoma Road). After the manufacturing of pottery started, the front of the small building was used as a showroom to display the pottery that was for sale.

On the night of November 10, 1938, the new plant caught fire. The fire department would not answer calls outside the city limits, so the little factory was completely destroyed with the exception of a handful of molds.

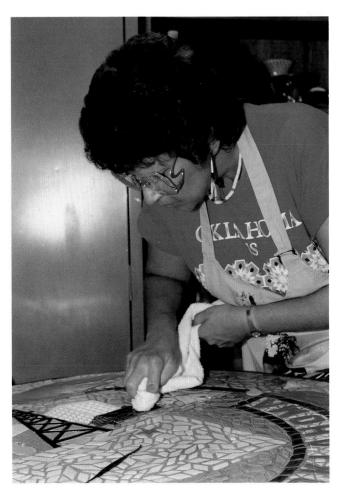

Joniece Frank, putting the finishing touch to her Mosaic Seal of the City of Sapulpa. It now hangs on the wall just inside Sapulpa's City Hall.

When money was available once again, rebuilding began. New molds were made, some from pieces salvaged from the fire. Production began again.

Through the years Frankoma went through many trials, disappointments and even bankruptcy, but the Franks never gave up. They always believed that God would bring them through, on top, and He did.

Frankoma continued to grow and expand until, at it's peak, over one hundred and forty people were employed. John Frank passed away in 1973 and his daughter Joniece took over the business with the help of her mother, Grace Lee.

Joniece grew up playing in the pottery plant and began working with her parents at the age of twelve. She directed plant tours and waited on customers when she was not in school. At this early age, her ambition was to follow in the footsteps of her father.

Through her and Frankoma's growing years, Joniece became well acquainted with all the operations of the pottery business from the mold shop to the retail showroom. Joniece graduated from the Hockaday College Preparatory School in Dallas, and went on to attend the University of Oklahoma, studying art. She worked closely with her father's friend and former associate, Joseph R. Taylor. Joniece graduated with a Bachelor of Fine Arts Degree in Sculpture, then went on to study a short while in Europe.

In 1960 Joniece began working alongside her father designing pottery. At the age of twenty-three she submitted one of her sculptures at the annual Oklahoma Artist's Exhibit and won first place. Many exceptional pieces of art have come from her creative hands.

Besides being the only designer, Joniece was president and chairman of the board of Frankoma from 1972 to 1991. During this period she had several challenges, but the greatest one came on September 26, 1983, when Frankoma had a second disastrous fire. Everything was lost, except for production molds that were in a fireproof room, thanks to the foresight of her father. In rebuilding after the 1938 fire, John Frank had a fireproof room built to house master molds. As the number of molds grew and fireproof space became limited, the discontinued master molds were stored in an attic above the plant. All those molds were destroyed in this 1983 fire.

Rebuilding began and Frankoma's reopening was celebrated in July of 1984. Since that time Frankoma has been in a constant battle for survival.

In April, 1990, the IRS closed Frankoma's doors because of past due taxes. Two weeks later Joniece filed for Chapter 11 bankruptcy protection, allowing her to resume control of the business and reopen.

In February, 1991, Richard Bernstein, a Maryland investor, purchased Frankoma Pottery, ending the family owned business of fifty-eight years.

Joniece continues to work for the new organization. Grace Lee, Joniece and Donna are still living in Sapulpa.

BUFFALO 4"   No. 119
Circa 1934-35   Glaze-Desert Gold
Designed by Ray Murray
BUFFALO 3 1/2"   No. 119
Circa 1934-35   Glaze-Black
Notice the different sizes. The Buffalo on the left is larger and has more pronounced detail, yet both were made about the same time.

TRADEMARKS

John Frank signed all his early pieces of pottery JOHN FRANK or ⅃F (his initials superimposed) along with the date. After the ceramic department was established at the University of Oklahoma, a logo was designed for marking the pottery made on the campus. This mark, we'll refer to as the OU Tepee, is just that, an Indian tepee with the letters OU as pictured:

John Frank used this logo to mark his pottery. With it he added his initials and usually the date. The OU Tepee logo was not exclusively for his use, many pieces have been found with this mark that have belonged to OU students. This trademark was a metal seal impressed by hand.

In the summer of 1933 John began producing and selling pottery in small quantities for his company, which went by the name of "FRANK POTTERIES." We have always found this pottery to bear a black ink mark which was applied by hand with a rubber stamp after firing. It reads:

FRANK POTTERIES
NORMAN, OKLAHOMA

In February of 1934 Frankoma Potteries was incorporated. At this time Mr. Frank began marking his pottery with a small block lettered "FRANKOMA" logo stamped with black ink. It soon became an incised mark, instead of ink.

One of the first sculptures Joseph Taylor designed for John Frank to reproduce was a pacing leopard (ocelot). Sometime in the latter part of 1935, Mr. Frank designed a new logo for Frankoma Potteries. He used Taylor's leopard, pacing upon the name Frankoma and added a tall vase in the background. The leopard represented Sculpture and the vase represented Pottery. This pacing leopard, often referred to as the "cat-mark," is always found incised.

Every incised trademark required each item, while still in the clay state, to be impressed by hand with a metal stamp (seal) in the mold. All early seals used for making trademarks were destroyed in the fire of November 10, 1938.

After the fire, Mr. Frank once again used a small block lettered "FRANKOMA" trademark which was also incised (by hand). This one was slightly larger than the earlier (1934) block lettered "FRANKOMA." An easy way to discern the older mark from the newer is by the letter "O" in the name FRANKOMA. The letter "O" is a perfect circle in the earliest mark. The letter "O" in the mark used after the fire is an oblong (skinny) letter. In the late forties Frankoma also began using the gummed label, "ORIGINAL CREATION by FRANKOMA," and did so until the fire of 1983.

Around 1950 the size of the trademark began to grow. Each letter in the name was a little larger and was still impressed by hand. About 1955 the trademark became a part of the mold, no longer having to be applied by hand.

Pottery made before 1942 does not bear a mold number. Sometimes it was penciled on the clay on items made prior to 1942. Since 1942 the mold number is usually incised on the bottom of each piece unless space limits will not permit one.

Many of the Frankoma miniatures have been popular souvenir items. Sometime during the war years these were occasionally stamped "MADE IN OKLAHOMA U.S.A." or "MADE IN USA" in black ink.

Prior to 1933...	JOHN FRANK (or) ⅃F	Incised
Or		Incised
1933-34...	FRANK POTTERIES NORMAN, OKLAHOMA	Black Ink
February 1934-35...	FRANKOMA (Circle "O")	Black Ink or Incised
1936 to November 1938...		Incised
1940s...	FRANKOMA (Oblong "O")	Incised
Early 1950s...	FRANKOMA (Larger)	Incised
After 1955...	FRANKOMA	In Mold
Since 1960...	⅃F	Personal Mark of Joniece Frank
Mark on Small Objects...		In Mold

FRANKOMA CLAYS

In the summer of 1933, John Frank began producing Oklahoma's first commercial pottery. His desire was for it to be made with Oklahoma clay.

While teaching at OU, he had the opportunity to work in the field with geological survey people, searching for and locating Oklahoma mineral deposits. This gave him first hand knowledge of possible sources for his clay. He experimented with specimens from all over the state. He chose a large clay deposit in the Arbuckle Mountains near Ada.

Three day trips were made regularly to the Arbuckle Mountains for this special clay. John Frank personally selected the clay veins, for it was crucial that the right vein was dug. He and two hired men dug, loaded and hauled the clay back to Sapulpa on an old sideboard truck. These trips continued through the years. Sometime in 1953 a good clay deposit was discovered in Sugar Loaf Hill near Sapulpa. The transition, from using the light tan Ada clay to using the brick red Sapulpa clay, was not completed until the end of 1954. Pottery made from that time until the 1980s can easily be identified by the brick red clay.

Frankoma began using an additive to strengthen the clay in the 1980s. This additive has caused the clay to lighten to a reddish pink color.

CLAY COLOR SUMMARY

YEARS	COLOR
1933-1954	Tan
1955-1980s	Brick Red
1980s-Today	Reddish Pink

GLAZE COLORS

In the early years of Frankoma, much experimenting with colors was necessary to obtain the desired color of glazes. For this reason a great variety of glazes are found from those early years, some unidentifiable.

John Frank, with the aid of his associate, J. W. Daugherty, developed some unique glazes using rutile, a mineral containing titanium dioxide. By special application, this type of glaze allows the clay to show through in part, giving the impression of having two glaze colors.

When Frankoma changed clays in 1954, from the light tan Ada clay to Sapulpa's brick red clay, this greatly effected the rutile glazes. The soft golden brown color which appeared in the Desert Gold and Prairie Green glazes changed to dark brown, because of the dark red clay.

The rutile glazes were effected once again in 1970. The rutile had always been purchased from special mines in the United States. In 1970 these mines were closed. Frankoma had to go to Australia to get the rutile necessary for this glaze. The difference in the two country's rutiles caused another drastic change in color. The deep rich colors of the glazes was gone. The colors mellowed. Therefore, since 1970 the rutile glazes are subdued.

To help you better identify these differences, we have indicated with each picture (if rutile glazes are pertinent) Ada clay or Sapulpa's red clay and pre- or post-1970. We give the glaze color(s) with every picture.

Following the list of all the Frankoma glazes, with the dates of availability, we are picturing some glazes that seem to have caused most identification problems.

By studying this color guide you are sure to become a pro at identifying Frankoma's glazes.

VERDE GREEN	(Translucent Emerald)	1933-36
POMPEIAN BRONZE	(Dark Green w/patches of Burnt Gold)	1933-38
DESERT GOLD (Early)	(Ivory & Gold)	1933-38
DESERT GOLD *(Rutile)	(Creamy Beige & Golden Brown)	1939-SA
BLUE GRAY JADE	(Blue Green)	1933-42
OSAGE BROWN	(Mottled w/hint of Orange)	1933-42
ONYX BLACK	(High Gloss) Earliest sometimes Iridescent	1933-SA
PATINA/VERDE BRONZE	(Green & Brown)	1933-SA
(Some early pieces glazed heavy-color is all green)		
Renamed PRAIRIE GREEN *(Rutile) in 1939		
ROYAL BLUE		1934-42
DOVE GRAY		1934-38
GUNMETAL		1934-38
CHEROKEE RED	(Dark Murky Plum)	1934-38
IVORY		1934-42
FAWN BROWN	(Butterscotch)	1934-42
OLD GOLD	(Semi-Mat Yellow)	1934-42
JADE GREEN	(Slightly Bluer than Silver Sage)	1934-38
SILVER SAGE	(Waxy Jade Green)	Circa 1942
DUSTY ROSE	(Mat Dull Pink)	Circa 1942
SKY BLUE		Circa 1942
PEACOCK BLUE	(Turquoise with patches of dark blue, originally Indian Blue)	1942-50
WHITE SAND		1942-SA
RED BUD	(Mottled Orchid/ Lilac)	1949-54
TURQUOISE	(Translucent)	1956-57
SORGHUM BROWN	(Very Dark Brown)	1951-54
CLAY BLUE	(Satiny Blue)	1953-61
BUCKSKIN TAN		1954 Only
SADDLE BROWN		1954 Only
TERRA COTTA ROSE	(Glossy Pink)	1955-57

SUNFLOWER YELLOW	(Yellow w/ Brown Specks)	1958-60
BROWN SATIN *(Rutile)	(Two Shades of Brown)	1958-94
WOODLAND MOSS *(Rutile)	(Blue & Brown)	1960-78
PEACH GLOW *(Rutile)	(Peach & Brown)	1962-74
FLAME	(Red Orange)	1964-92
FLAT BLACK		1973-75
COFFEE	(Medium Brown)	1973-88
RUBBED BISQUE	(Wood Tone)	1973-SA
AUTUMN YELLOW		1975-90
FREEDOM RED	(Bright Red)	1976-78
BLUE	(Medium Blue)	1976-78
ROBIN EGG BLUE	(Blue w/Dk. Blue Specks)	1979-92
TERRA COTTA	(Clay Color)	1980-SA
OLIVE GREEN		1982 Only
WISTERIA	(Lilac)	1983-85
NAVY		1985-SA
MOUNTAIN HAZE	(Light Bluish Gray)	1987-92
COUNTRY BLUE	(Navy w/White Spots)	1988-SA
PEACH		1989-92
TEAL		1990-SA
MAUVE	(Light Rose)	1992-93
CABERNET	(Maroon)	1992-SA
FOREST	(Dark Green)	1993-SA
BONE		1993-SA
COBALT		1994-SA
PLUM	(Dark Purple)	1994-SA

*Rutile Glaze...Definite Color changes after 1954 and 1970.

Frankoma's plans are to discontinue the Prairie Green and Desert Gold glazes in 1995.

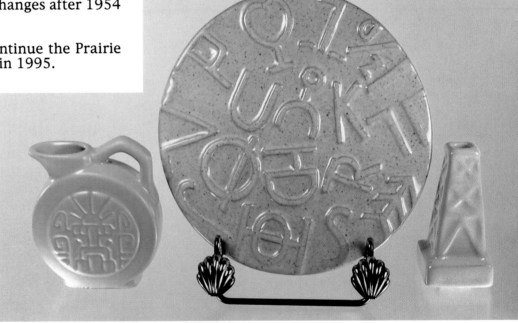

IVORY Miniature Teapot 2" Mark: 1934-35
DOVE GRAY Bud Vase
WHITE SAND Miniature Puma

OLD GOLD Miniature Aztec Pitcher
SUNFLOWER YELLOW Cattlebrand Trivet
AUTUMN YELLOW Miniature Tepee Vase

SKY BLUE Miniature Donkey
PEACOCK BLUE Miniature Vase
CLAY BLUE Miniature Walking Elephant
ROYAL BLUE Miniature Aztec Pitcher

PRAIRIE GREEN (POST-1970)
Dogwood Candleholder
PRAIRIE GREEN (PRE-1970)
RED CLAY Candleholder
PRAIRIE GREEN, ADA CLAY
Peter Pan Mask

DESERT GOLD, ADA CLAY
Stein
DESERT GOLD (PRE-1970)
RED CLAY War God Mug
DESERT GOLD (POST-1970)
Bud Vase No. 46

WOODLAND MOSS (POST-1970) Free Form Vase No. 21
WOODLAND MOSS (PRE-1970) Fan Dancer

PEACH GLOW (PRE-1970) Cornucopia
PEACH GLOW (POST-1970) Hexagonal Vase No. 65
PEACH GLOW (PRE-1970) Single Candleholder

BROWN SATIN (PRE-1970) Pedestalled Bowl No. 238
BROWN SATIN (POST-1970) Seated Puma

FRANKOMA'S GLAZES TODAY (1994)
CABERNET, COUNTRY BLUE, NAVY, TEAL, FOREST, BLACK,
PRAIRIE GREEN, BROWN SATIN, TERRA COTTA, DESERT GOLD,
BONE, WHITE SAND, (New Colors: COBALT AND PLUM, not
illustrated). Boot Mug No. C33

FRANK POTTERIES

PINNACLE VASE 6 3/4" Desert Gold
VASE 4" Prairie Green
VASE 6 1/2" Prairie Green

VASE 12 1/2"
Designed by John Frank

FLOWER BOWL 2" Blue
VASE 3 3/4" Osage Brown
VASE 2 5/8" Verde Green

LARGE INDIAN JAR H-7"
Prairie Green
Circumference is 27"
The Indian Jar was produced by
Frankoma until 1938, then reis-
sued in 1949 with minor modifi-
cations for only one year. All are
very rare.

FRANKOMA DISPLAY SIGNS

Frankoma has produced display signs, since the late thirties, exclusively for their dealers to use with their pottery set-ups. Today they are also available for the public to purchase.

PACING LEOPARD SIGN
L-8 5/8"
Glaze-Prairie Green, Ada Clay
This was their first dealer sign, available around 1936. It was destroyed in the 1938 fire and never remade.

THIRD FRANKOMA SIGN L-7 1/2"
Glaze-Desert Gold (Pre-1970), Red Clay
Was used from the early 1950s until 1960.

FOURTH FRANKOMA SIGN L-7"
Glaze-Flame
In 1960, Joniece Frank designed this fourth display sign. It is still used today and is the only sign that has ever been sold to the public.

TEPEE SIGN H-6 1/2" Glaze-Prairie Green, Ada Clay
Second dealer sign, produced around 1941 and used through the forties.

SCULPTURES

FISH FLOWER FROG 4 1/2"   No. 404
Circa 1935-38   Glaze-Jade Green

COATI-MUNDI   H-4 3/8"
I-1933 D-1938 (Fire) Glaze-Early Desert Gold
Designed by Joseph Taylor

WALKING OCELOT L-10 1/2"   No. 104
I-1934 D-1938 (Fire)   Glaze-Ivory
Designed by Joseph Taylor
CHARGING TIGER L-13"   No. 103
I-1934 D-1938 (Fire) Glaze-Iridescent Black
Designed by Joseph Taylor

DEER GROUP   H-8 1/4"   No. 109
I-1933 D-1938 (Fire) Glaze-Prairie Green
Designed by Joseph Taylor

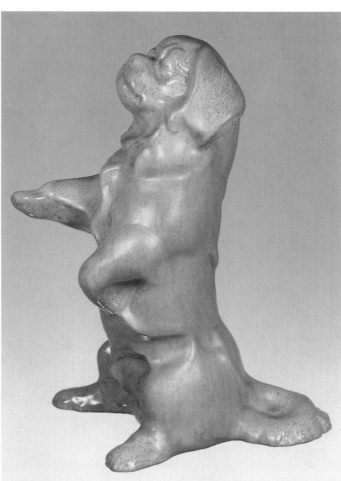

SWAN FLOWER FROG H-4"
I-1936 D-1938 (Fire) Glaze-Ivory

MERMAID FLOWER FROG H-7"
Circa 1933-34
Designed by Joseph Taylor

PEKINGESE DOG 7 3/4" No. 112
I-1934 D-1938 (Fire) Glaze-Desert Gold
Designed by Joseph Taylor

HOUND DOG H-5 1/2"
Circa 1934-35
Glaze-Ivory

PRANCING PERCHERON H-4 3/4" No. 108
I-1933 D-1938 (Fire) Glaze-Ivory
Designed by Joseph Taylor

COYOTE PUP H-7 3/4" No. 105
I-1934 D-1938 (Fire) Glaze-Prairie Green
Designed by Joseph Taylor

REARING CLYDESDALE 6 3/4" No. 107
I-1933 D-1942 Reissued 1973-75
Glaze-Prairie Green, Ada Clay
Designed by Joseph Taylor

CIRCUS HORSE 4 1/2" No. 138
I-1934 D-1955 Glaze-Cherokee Red
Designed by Joseph Taylor

PRANCING COLT H-8" No. 117
I-1935 D-1952 Glaze-Prairie Green
Designed by Joseph Taylor

CAMEL   6"
Circa 1934-35   Glaze-Iridescent Black

COWBOY   7 1/2"
Circa 1934-35   Glaze-Osage Brown
COWBOY   7 3/4"
Circa 1934-35   Glaze-Osage Brown
"RODEO" is incised on the brim of this Cowboy's hat and
"WOODWARD OKLA." around the base.
Recent findings indicate the Cowboy was actually produced
in 1934-35 rather than during the late thirties or early for-
ties as first reported.

COWBOY   7 1/2"   Glaze-Osage Brown
COWBOY   7 1/2"   Glaze-Ivory
Notice brim of hat is pinched.
These four Cowboys have the 1934-35 Frankoma mark.

INDIAN BOWL MAKER 6" No. 123
I-1934   D-1952   Reissued 1973-93
Glaze-Cherokee Red
Designed by Joseph Taylor
INDIAN BOWL MAKER 6 3/4"
Glaze-Osage Brown
A 1934 piece marked "TAYLOR".

TAOS SQUAW H-8 1/4" No. 143
I-1934 D-1938 (Fire)
Glaze-Osage brown
Very Rare!

FANDANCER   8 1/2"   No. 113
I-1934   D-1969   Reissued 1973-76
Glaze-Flat Black
Designed by Joseph Taylor
FANDANCER (Early) 9"   Glaze-Ivory

HARLAM HOOFER
(NEGRO DANCER)
H-13" No. 127
Circa 1934-35
Glaze-Pompeian Bronze
Designed by Joseph Taylor

INDIAN CHIEF   8"   No. 142
I-1938   D-1953   Reissued 1973-93
Glaze-Prairie Green, Ada Clay
Designed by Ray Murray
INDIAN CHIEF   Hand Painted
Circa 1950

FANDANCER With No. 5P **DEEP PLATTER**   L-16"
Glaze-Prairie Green
Occasionally the Fandancer was purchased with the deep platter in a matching glaze. Very few matching sets have been found.

TORCH SINGER
H-13 1/2" No. 126
Circa 1934-35
Designed by Joseph Taylor

TORCH SINGER & HARLAM HOOFER
Glaze-Ivory

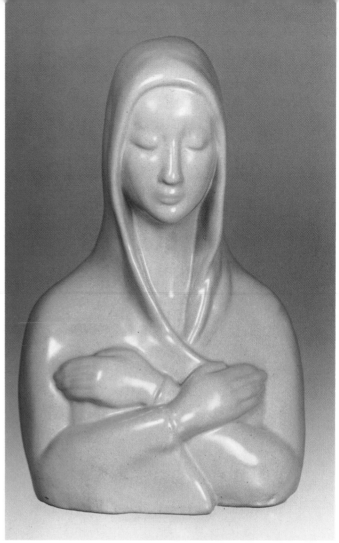

MADONNA H-8"
Circa 1940   Glaze-Ivory

AMAZON WOMAN   H-8"   No. 101
I-1933   D-1935   Glaze-Gunmetal
Designed by Joseph Taylor

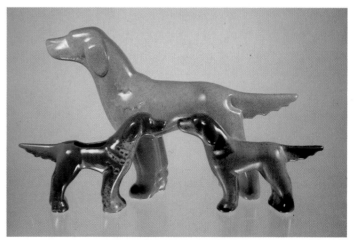

ENGLISH SETTERS, MINIATURES   2 7/8"
The piece on the left has been hollowed out making it a min-
iature vase. Both are glazed in Prairie Green, the one on the
left has a very thin glaze.
LARGE ENGLISH SETTER 5 1/2"   No. 141
I-1942   D-1949   Glaze-Fawn Brown

From Left: **GARDENER GIRL**
H-5 3/4"   No. 701
I-1942   D-1952
GARDENER BOY H-7" No. 702
I-1942   D-1949
Wearing belted pants and shirt.
FLOWER GIRL   H-5 1/2"
No. 700
I-1942   D-1952
GARDENER BOY H-7" No. 702
I-1950   D-1952
Wearing bibbed overalls and shirt.

Top Left: **BULL**   H-2"   No. 166
I-1942 ONLY   Glaze-Silver Sage
TROJAN HORSE
H-2 1/2"   No. 162
I-1942   D-1957 Glaze-Redbud
SWAN   H-3"   No. 168
I-1936   D-1957 Glaze-Ivory
DONKEY H-2 3/4"   No. 164
I-1942 ONLY   Glaze-Sky Blue
Bottom Left: **TERRIER**
H-2 7/8"   No. 161
I-1942 ONLY

Glaze-Royal Blue
PUMA   H-3"   No. 165
I-1942   D-1957
Glaze-Desert Gold, Ada Clay
ELEPHANT   H-3"   No. 160
I-1942 ONLY
Glaze-Dusty Rose
ENGLISH SETTER
H-2 7/8"   No. 163
I-1942   D-1957
Glaze-Prairie Green, Ada Clay

GARDENER BOYS Rear view

TWO GIRLS 5"
Circa Early Forties
The two girls were meant to represent Donna Ruth and Joniece at that age.

WILLARD STONE SCULPTURES

From Left: **INDIAN MAIDEN** H-13" No. 101
I-1963 ONLY   Reissued 1973-SA
COYOTE   H-12 1/2"   No. 102
I-1963 ONLY   Reissued 1973-SA
SQUIRREL   H-6"   No. 105
I-1973-SA
INDIAN MADONNA   H-14"   No. 104
I-1986-SA
MARE AND COLT   H-12"   No. 103
I-1963 ONLY   Reissued 1973-SA
Glazed in Rubbed Bisque and White Sand

MEDICINE MAN H-8 1/2" No. 115
I-1941-42 Reissued 1973-75 Glaze-Rubbed Bisque
Designed by Acee Blue Eagle

PONY TAIL GIRL H-10"   No. 106
I-1986-SA   Glaze-Peach
Designed by Joniece Frank

BOOK ENDS

PRANCING COLT BOOK END H-5"
Circa 1934-35 Glaze-Osage Brown

SEATED FIGURE BOOK END
5 1/2"   No. 425
I-1934   D-1938 (Fire)
Glaze-Ivory
Designed by Joseph Taylor
The master mold for this piece was
destroyed by the fire and a new
master mold was made from an
existing one. A 3/4" base was
added and renamed as seen at the
right.
MOUNTAIN GIRL BOOK END
5 3/4"   No. 425
I-After November 1938   D-1942
Glaze-Prairie Green
Reissued 1973-75 No. 136

WALKING OCELOT BOOK ENDS H-3" x 7"   No. 424
I-1934   D-1938 (Fire)   Glaze-Fawn Brown
Designed by Joseph Taylor
Looking close "TAYLOR" can be seen on the back-side of the
book end.

LEOPARD BOOK ENDS
H-4 1/2" x 8 1/2"   No. 421
I-1934   D-1942
Glaze-Heavy Prairie Green
Reissued 1973 ONLY   No. 112
Designed by Joseph Taylor
Renamed PACING OCELOT some-
time before 1942.

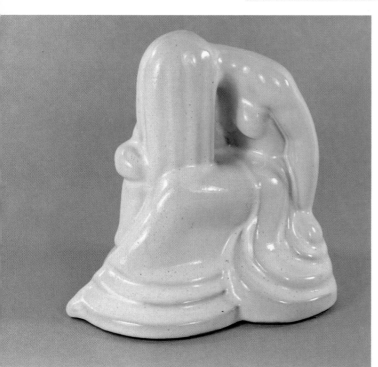

DREAMER GIRL (WEEPING LADY) H-5 3/8"   No. 427
I-1938   D-1954 Glaze-White Sand
Designed by a student of Mr. Franks, name unknown.

BUCKING BRONCO BOOK END
5 1/2"   No. 423
I-1942   D-1949
Glaze-Prairie Green
Designed by Joseph Taylor
CHARGER HORSE BOOK END
6"   No. 420
I-1934   D-1960
Glaze-Desert Gold, Ada Clay
Reissued in 1973-75   No. 111
Designed by Joseph Taylor

BOOT BOOK ENDS
7"   No. 433
I-1951-SA
Glaze-Prairie Green, Red Clay
Designed by John Frank

**Opposite page
center right:**

SEAHORSE BOOK ENDS
H-5"   No. 426
I-1934   D-1938 (Fire)
Glaze-Prairie Green
Designed by John Frank

RED IRISH SETTER BOOK END
6 1/2"   No. 430
I-1942   D-1960
Glaze-Prairie Green, Ada Clay
Designed by Craig Shephard
This is an early piece, notice the
thickness of the neck. It was later
stylized as the one pictured on the
right.
RED IRISH SETTER BOOK END
6 1/2"   No. 430
I-1942   D-1960
Glaze-Brown Satin, Pre-1970
Reissued 1973-75, No. 120

COLLIE HEAD (SHORT HAIR)
7"
Early 1970s   Glaze-Prairie Green
Designed by Joniece Frank
COLLIE HEAD (LONG HAIR)
7"   No. 122
I-1973-75   Glaze-Rubbed Bisque
Designed by Bernard Frazier
These were first produced in the
early 1950s for the Collie Club of
America to be given as trophies. In
the early '70s the Collie Club re-
quested a short hair Collie (pictured left) to accommodate that
breed.

MASK AND WALL POCKETS

SMALL NEGRO MASK
H-3 1/4"
Circa 1940 Glaze-Early Blue
MINIATURE INDIAN MASK
H-3 3/4"
I-1934 D-1957 Reissued 1973-75
Glaze-Royal Blue

INDIAN HEAD WALL POCKET w/FULL HEADDRESS H-4"
Circa 1936-38 Glaze-Cherokee Red
Very rare!

"HAPPY INDIAN" MASK 5"
Circa-1942 Glaze-Osage Brown
Very rare!

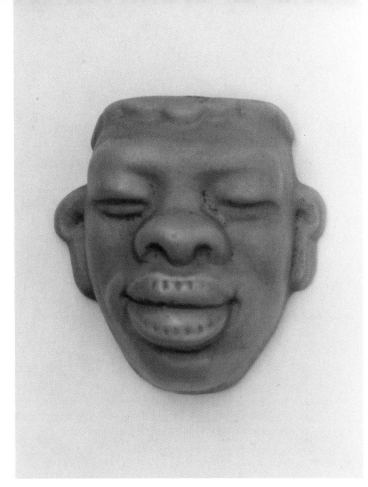

**NEGRO HEAD
WALL POCKET**

H-2 1/2" Glaze-Clear
Circa 1940

**INDIAN HEAD WALL
POCKET**

H-3" Glaze-Early Blue
Circa 1936-38
This Indian Head Wall Pocket has
been found more often than the
one on page 26 with the full
headdress.

WALL POCKET W/WATERER L-4 1/2"   No. A1
I-1951 Only   Glaze-Desert Gold, Ada Clay

BIRD HANDLE WALL POCKET   H-5"
I-1942 Only Glaze-Prairie Green, Ada Clay

PHOEBE WALL POCKET H-7 1/2" No. 730
I-1948-49   Reissued 1951-52, No. 194; 1973-75, No. 130
The hand painted Phoebes were probably made during 1951-52 by Ocee Sams.

BILIKEN WALL POCKET H-7"
Circa 1951-55   Glaze-Prairie Green, Ada Clay
Probably marked with one of the following (or similar) marks:
   JESTER'S DAY   TULSA COURT   MUSKOGEE COURT
   MAY 7-8, 1954 or   No. 47   or   No. 99
   HOST   R.O.J.
K.S. BOOT'S ADAMS
(Photographed)

RAM'S HEAD WALL POCKET H-6"   No. 193
I-1942 Only Glaze-Prairie Green, Ada Clay

LEAF WALL POCKET   12"   No. 196
I-1964   D-1966   Glaze-Prairie Green, Red Clay
LEAF WALL POCKET   8 1/2"   No. 197
I-1964   D-1966   Glaze-Desert Gold, Red Clay

WAGON WHEEL WALL POCKET   H-7"
I-1949   D-1953   Glaze-Desert Gold, Ada Clay

BOOT WALL POCKET   5"
Circa 1960s   Glaze-Brown Satin, Red Clay
DUTCH SHOE WALL POCKET   8 1/2"   No. 913
Dated 1955   Glaze-Desert Gold, Red Clay
Frankoma produced a 9" Dutch Shoe Planter from 1958-60
and reissued from 1974-91, mold #913.

CANDLEHOLDERS

CANDLEHOLDER 2 1/2"
No. 300
I-1936-42 Reissued 1980-81
Glaze-Blue Gray Jade
SPIRAL CANDLEHOLDERS
2 1/2" No. 305
I-1936 D-1938 (Fire) Glaze-
Desert Gold

CANDELABRUM 11 3/4"
No. 306
I-1936 D-1942 Glaze-Prairie
Green

THE MONKS 4 1/2"
No. 308
Circa 1934-35 Glaze-Ivory,
Royal Blue
Could also be used as bud vases.

DOUBLE CANDLEHOLDERS
4 1/4" No. 304
I-1936 D-1976 Glaze-Dusty
Rose

SHELL CANDLEHOLDER
4 1/2" No. 314
I-1942 Only
Glaze-Prairie Green, Ada Clay

DOUBLE CACTUS
CANDLEHOLDER 8" No. 306
I-1949 Only Glaze-Redbud

PEDESTALLED
CANDLEHOLDER
4 1/2" No. 301
I-1964-67 Reissued 1982-83,
No. 747
Glaze-Prairie Green (Pre-1970) Red
Clay

DOGWOOD CANDLEHOLDER
5 1/2" No. 300
I-1965-79 Reissued 1982-83, No.
733
Glaze-Prairie Green (Post-1970)
Red Clay

SINGLE CANDLEHOLDERS
5 1/2" No. 305
I-1950-78 Reissued 1982-83,
No. 732
Glaze-Prairie Green (Pre-1970) Red
Clay

WAGON WHEEL
CANDLEHOLDER
Diam-6 1/2"
I-1983 Only Glaze-Coffee

WAGON WHEEL ASH TRAY/
CANDLEHOLDER
6 1/2" No. 454
I-1951 D-1964
Glaze-Prairie Green, Ada Clay

"ROCKS" CANDLEHOLDERS
Diam-4 1/2"
Circa 1970s
Glaze-Prairie Green (Post-1970)

PILLAR CANDLEHOLDER
4 3/4" No. 311
I-1968-75 Reissued 1982-83,
No. 738
Glaze-Prairie Green (Post-1970)

SMOKING PARAPHERNALIA

HUMIDOR   H-6 1/2"
I-1934-35   Glaze-Ivory

ASHTRAY 3 1/4" x 4" No. 3/303
I-1942 Only   Glaze-Silver Sage
BOOK ASHTRAY 3" x 3 1/2"
I-1936   Glaze-Fawn Brown
Book edge reads: 1936 Vol II
ASHTRAY   3 1/4" x 4"
I-1942 Only   Glaze-Prairie Green

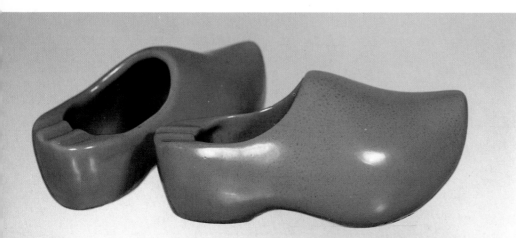

DUTCH SHOE ASHTRAYS
(Right & Left)   6"   No. 466
I-1958   D-1960 Glaze-Clay Blue

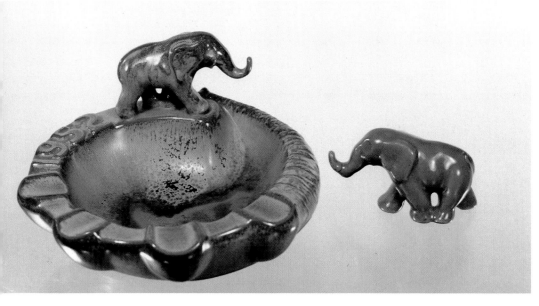

ELEPHANT ASHTRAY
Diam-6 1/2" No. 459
I-1951-52
Glaze-Prairie Green, Ada Clay
Ash trays dated "1952" were made during the "Eisenhower for President" campaign to help sponsor the Republican party.
WALKING ELEPHANT
H-1 3/4"
I-1951 D-1957   Glaze-Clay Blue

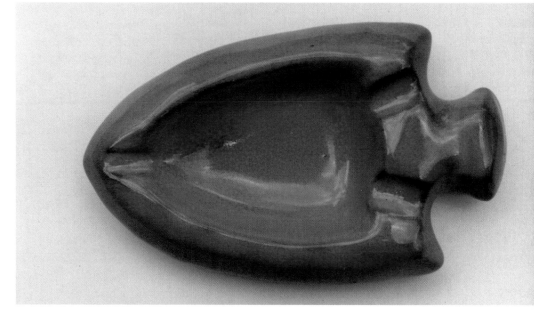

ARROWHEAD ASHTRAY   7"
No. 453
I-1953 SA
Glaze-Turquoise, Red Clay

FREE FORM ASHTRAY
10" No. 30
I-1957   D-1980   Glaze-Terra Cotta Rose
From 1957-67 this tray had an open wrought iron handle as pictured, and changed in 1968-80 to a closed plated steel handle.

SILVER OVERLAY

In the early '40s, Frankoma's sales representative for New York state had shipments of appropriate vases (finished pieces) sent to a New York silversmith to be decorated by silver overlay. Most are marked "STERLING" somewhere in the pattern. All we've seen are decorated over Frankoma's Prairie Green glaze. These are all very beautiful!

GRECIAN VASE

LEAF HANDLED VASE

ROUND JAR

TALL FLAT VASE

FIRESIDE VASE

CHINESE BOTTLE VASE   9"
No. 14
I-1934   D-1942 Glaze-Chinese
Red
Very rare color.

TALL RAM'S HEAD VASE   9 1/4"   No. 74
I-1934   D-1938 (Fire)   Glaze-Jade
SMALL RAM'S HEAD VASE   6" No. 38
I-1934   D-1949   Glaze-Jade

35

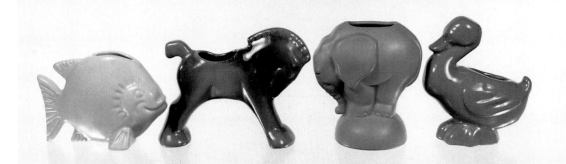

FISH FLOWER HOLDER 3 5/8" No. 185
I-1942 Only Glaze-Old Gold
HOBBY HORSE FLOWER HOLDER 3 1/2" No. 182
I-1942 Only Glaze-Peacock Blue
ELEPHANT FLOWER HOLDER 3 1/2" No. 180
I-1942 Only Glaze-Dusty Rose
DUCK FLOWER HOLDER 3 3/4" No. 184
I-1942 Only Glaze-Sky Blue

IVY BOWL 4 1/2" No. 37
I-1936 D-1938 (Fire) Glaze-Desert Gold
A second Ivy Bowl #27 was produced from 1950-57, pictured in "Frankoma Treasures".

LEAF HANDLED VASE 10" No. 71
I-1939 D-1993 Glaze-Blue Gray Jade, Ada Clay
John Frank threw the #71 on the potter's wheel during the reconstruction period after the fire of November 10, 1938. It was his "Phoenix" that would raise Frankoma from the ashes to live again. It was discontinued December 31, 1993.

CENTERPIECE BOWL 18"
No. 219
I-1942 D-1966 Glaze-Prairie
Green, Ada Clay

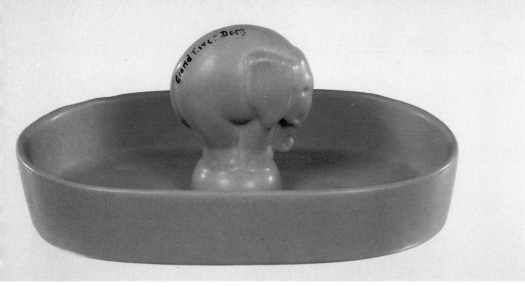

OVAL LOW BOWL 7" No.211
Circa 1942   Glaze-Dusty Rose
Bowl may be found with a miniature attached in the center.

SMALL ROUND JAR 3 3/4"   No. 6
Circa 1942   Glaze-Ivory
ROUND JAR 5"   No. 24
I-1934   D-1949   Glaze-Turquoise
MINT BOWL 3 3/4" No. 35
I-1936-61 Reissued 1964-67 Glaze-Prairie Green,Ada Clay
The footed rim was changed in the 1964 issue.
SMALL MINT BOWL 3" No. 34
I-1936   D-1938 (Fire)   Glaze-Desert Gold

GRECIAN VASE 10" No. 50C
Circa 1942 Glaze-Terra Cotta,
Prairie Green Handles
The 1942 catalog reads: "Terra Cotta, hand-tooled with glazed handles". Inside glaze is Prairie Green.
GRECIAN VASE 9 1/2"
No. 50
I-1942 D-1952
Glaze-Prairie Green

FLAT VASE 6 1/2"   No. 40
I-1936   D-1938 (Fire)
Glaze-Dove Gray
SMALL FLAT VASE 4" No. 39
I-1934   D-1938 (Fire)
Glaze-Ivory
TALL CORNUCOPIA 7" No. 56
I-1942-49 Reissued 1968-75
Glaze-Desert Gold, Ada Clay
SMALL CORNUCOPIA 5" No.56K
Circa 1942   Glaze-Prairie Green

37

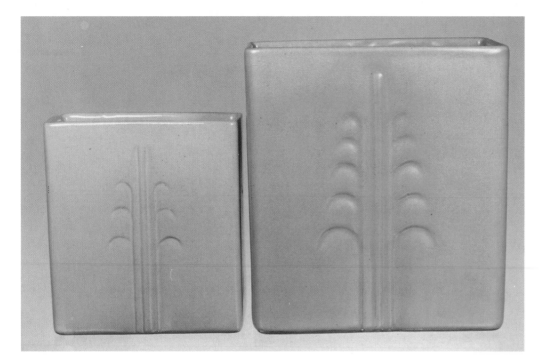

SMALL REED PILLOW VASE
4 1/2"   No. 61
Circa 1942   Glaze-Ivory
LARGE REED PILLOW VASE
6"   No. 60
Circa 1942   Glaze-Old Gold

FLOWERABRUM   11 1/2"
No. 58
Circa 1942   Glaze-Prairie Green

BLACK FOOTED VASE   4"
No. 55
I-1942   D-1967   Glaze-Blue
Gray Jade
An unusual #55, pierced around
the top with the #12 jewelry pat-
tern and glazed in pale pink. Other
pierced patterns have been found
on this vase.
BLACK FOOTED VASE   Glaze-
Desert Gold, Ada Clay

OBLONG FLOWER BOWL
L-10" No. 203
I-1938   D-1942   Glaze-Onyx
Black

LOW RECTANGULAR BOWL   L-7"   No. 62
I-1948   D-1953   Glaze-Prairie Green, Ada Clay
PILLOW VASE   7"   No. 63
I-1942   D-1967   Glaze-Desert Gold (Pre-1970), Red Clay
ORIENTAL PILLOW VASE   5"   No. 64
Circa 1942   Glaze-Peacock Blue

SQUARE BOWL   3"   No. 30
I-1936   D-1942   Glaze-Blue Gray Jade
ROUND BOWL   3"
Circa 1942   Glaze-Prairie Green
CARVED JAR   4 3/4"   No. 70
I-1934   D-1949   Glaze-Jade Green

FAN SHELL VASE   6"   No. 54
I-1942-65   Reissued 1980-88   Glaze-Desert Gold, Ada Clay

CHAMBERED NAUTILUS VASE 6" No. 54
I-1942 D-1956 Glaze-Turquoise, Red Clay

CORNUCOPIA BOWL 12" No. 222
I-1948-SA Glaze-Clay Blue, Red Clay
A larger Cornucopia #215 was available from 1942 through 1979.
CORNUCOPIA 9 1/2" No. 57
I-1942 D-1959 Glaze-Dusty Rose

VASE/HONEY BOTTLE 6 1/2" No. 832
Circa Early 1950s Glaze-Desert Gold, Ada Clay
This was in production later, from 1958-61.

MINI RINGED VASE 2 3/4"
No. 500
I-1942 D-1957 Glaze-Fawn
Brown
BUD VASE 5 1/2" No. 29
I-1934 D-1942 Glaze-Dove
Gray
BUD VASE 4 1/2" No. 505
I-1942 Only Glaze-Dusty Rose
SMALL BULBOUS VASE
2 3/4"
Circa 1934-35 Glaze-Royal Blue
MINI RINGED VASE Glaze-Peacock Blue

THUNDERBIRD PITCHER 5"
No. 59K
Glaze-Prairie Green, Ada Clay
Very rare!
THUNDERBIRD CANTEEN
6 1/2"   No. 59
I-1942   D-1983 Glaze-Prairie
Green, Ada Clay
**MINIATURE THUNDERBIRD
VASE** 3 1/2" No. 506
I-1942 Only   Glaze-Prairie
Green, Ada Clay
LARGE THUNDERBIRD VASE
5"
Glaze-Prairie Green, Ada Clay
Very rare!

MINI SNAIL PITCHER
2"   No. 558
I-1942   D-1951 Glaze-Old Gold
MINI PITCHER
2 1/2"   No. 556
I-1942   D-1951
Glaze-Prairie Green
Mold for the first Christmas card.
MINIATURE BOOT
3 1/2"   No. 507
I-1942-64 Glaze-Silver Sage
Reissued 1981-83 w/o Star
Notice the Frankoma sticker with
an Indian head.
VASE   3 1/2"   No. 502
I-1933   D-1942
Glaze-Onyx Black
MINIATURE VASE
2 3/4"   No. 502
I-1950-51   Glaze-Redbud
MINIATURE VASE
2 1/2"   No. 503
I-1950-51   Glaze-Prairie Green

FIRESIDE VASE & PITCHER   17" No. 77 & 77A
I-1942   D-1974 Glaze-Desert Gold (Pre-1970), Red Clay

SCALLOPED BOWL 12"   No. 218
I-1942-SA   Glaze-Clay Blue
DEEP FREE FORM BOWL 8"   No.234
I-1953-58   Reissued 1962-93   Glaze-Redbud, Ada Clay
The 1962 issue was restyled with a foot.

41

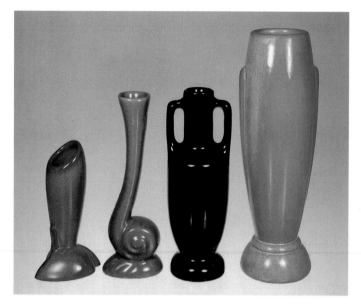

BUD VASE (MODERN)
4 1/2"   No. 32
I-1953   D-1975
Glaze-Brown Satin (Pre-1970)
SNAIL BUD VASE
6"   No. 31
I-1934   D-1991 Glaze-Clay Blue
TWO HANDLED BUD VASE
6 1/4"   No. 20
I-1964   D-1976
Glaze-Onyx Black
CROCUS BUD VASE
8"   No. 43
I-1934   D-1981
Glaze-Desert Gold, Ada Clay

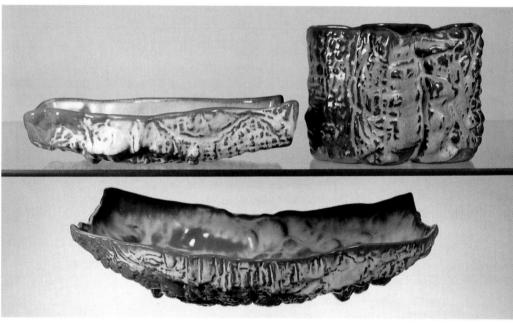

CORK BARK BOWL
9"   No. B4
I-1960   D-1961
Glaze-Desert Gold, Red Clay
CORK BARK PLANTER
4 1/2"   No. B3
I-1960   D-1991
Glaze-Prairie Green, Red Clay
CORK BARK BOWL
13"   No. B6
I-1960   D-1961
Glaze-Desert Gold, Red Clay

ROUND DEEP CACTUS BOWL
5"   No. 3
I-1949   D-1953   Glaze-Desert
Gold, Ada Clay
CORK BARK ROUND BOWL
10"   No. B7
I-1960   D-1961   Glaze-Desert
Gold, Red Clay

OBLONG BOWL   12"   No. 45
I-1955   D-1978
Glaze-Prairie Green, Red Clay

WAGON WHEEL VASE
7"   No. 94
I-1942   D-1961
Glaze-Prairie Green, Ada Clay
FREE FORM BUD VASE
9"   No. 41
I-1971   D-1975
Glaze-Brown Satin, Red Clay
FOOTED ROUND VASE
5"   No. 22S & 22A
I-1962   D-1991
Glaze-Prairie Green, Red Clay
In 1975 the mold number was
changed from 22S to 22A.

TALL URN   8"   No. 52
I-1953   D-1980 Glaze-Desert Gold (Pre-1970) Red Clay
THREE LEVEL VASE   9 1/2"   No. 58
I-1953   D-1964 Glaze-Desert Gold (Pre-1970) Red Clay

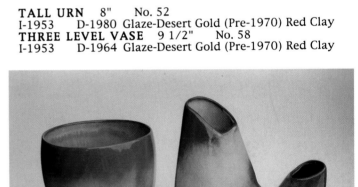

CORNUCOPIA   7"   No. 57
I-1962-70   Reissued 1980-91 Glaze-Black
SHELL BOWL   14"   No. 213
I-1942   D-1949   Glaze-Peacock Blue

PLANTER   8" x 3"   No. 17
I-1964   D-1991   Glaze-Brown
Satin (Pre-1970)
POD VASE 7"   No. 237
I-1964   D-1974 Glaze-Prairie
Green (Pre-1970)

CRESCENT BOWL 12 1/2"
No. 211
I-1950   D-1979 Glaze-Desert
Gold (Pre-1970) Red Clay

OLD FASHION PITCHER SET
Glaze-Robin Egg Blue
Pitcher 5 1/2" No. F30A,
Bowl 7" No. F30B I-1961-SA
A smaller set has also been available since 1963.

ALADDIN LAMP CANDLE-HOLDER 8 1/2" No. 309
I-1968   D-1970 Glaze-White
Sand

44

FREE FORM BOWL 12" No. 214
I-1950 D-1974 Glaze-Desert Gold (Pre-1970) Red Clay
FAN VASE 7" No. 19
I-1962 D-1974 Glaze-Prairie Green (Pre-1970) Red Clay
Was reissued in 1980-81, mold number 198.

SMALL SWAN PLANTER 7 1/2" No. 228
I-1950-SA Glaze-Wisteria
BASKET PLANTER 4 1/2" No. 188
I-1989 D-1991 Glaze-Mountain Haze
TURTLE PLANTER 7" No. 396
I-1983 D-1992 Glaze-Robin Egg Blue

POSTCARD 1952 5 1/2" x 6 1/2"
Back reads: "This is Joniece Frank showing the colors Frankoma Pottery is made in. Frankoma is recognized in the field of Ceramic Art because of their well designed pottery forms and earthen colors - Prairie Green, Desert Gold, Red Bud, Onyx Black, White Sand and Clay Blue. Frankoma is priced so that all can enjoy owning and using it. Each piece is made to be both USEFUL and BEAUTIFUL. Write for your completely illustrated 16 page catalog: FRANKOMA, Sapulpa, Oklahoma."

This postcard was also used on the cover of the 1952 catalog.

VARIOUS POSTCARDS
3 1/2" x 5 1/2"

"OKLAHOMA PLAINSMAN DINNERWARE"
Circa Early '50s
"FRANKOMA POTTERY"
Circa Early '50s
"MR. FRANK 'THROWING' ON THE POTTER'S WHEEL"
Circa 1950s

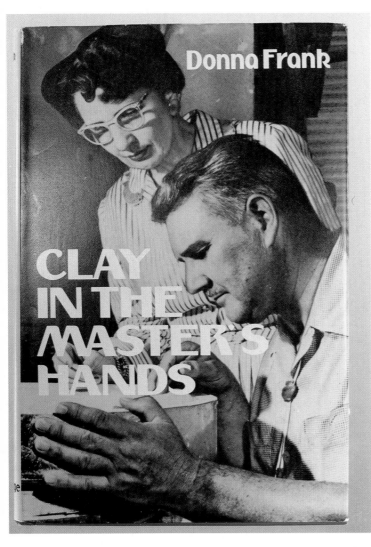

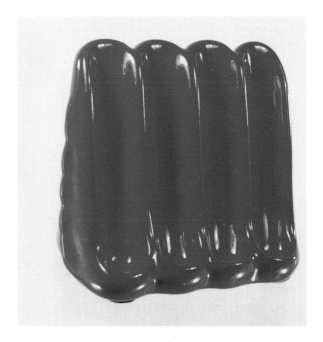

TOOTHBRUSH HOLDER
No. 401
I-1980   D-1991   Glaze-Flame

"CLAY IN THE MASTER'S HANDS" Book by Donna Frank. The Story of John Frank is affectionately told by his eldest daughter, Donna Frank. It was released in November of 1977. Although this book is now out of print, it is a must for anyone truly interested in this extraordinary family.

Donna and Joniece worked together on a revised (second) edition of "Clay In The Master's Hands". It became available in 1995.

DOG BANK 7 1/2"   No. 385
I-1980   D-1982   Glaze-Brown
Satin
COLLIE HEAD BANK 7 3/4"
Dated 1971   Glaze-Medium
Blue

BANK
Advertising "SOUTHEASTERN
STATE BANK TULSA" 4"
Glaze-Prairie Green (Pre-1970)
MALLARD BANK
4 3/4"   No. 382
I-1980   D-1983
Glaze-Autumn Yellow

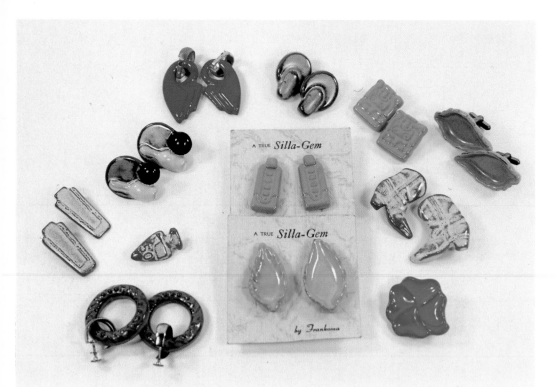

FRANKOMA JEWELRY 1955-1957
Ear clips, Ear screws, Cuff links and Dress pins. Notice the small Arrowhead pin just left of the "Silla Gem" cards. This pin was produced in 1957 for the Oklahoma's Semicentennial Celebration. Pictured is an outline of the State of Oklahoma and "50".

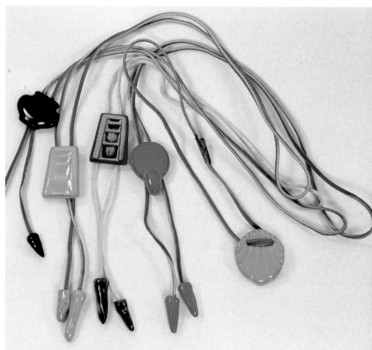

CACTI-PIN 1 1/2"
Circa 1943-45
Produced in eight different colors: Peacock Blue, Silver Sage, Old Gold, Ivory, Royal Blue, Dusty Rose, Prairie Green and the last color we are not sure of. These seven glazes are all we have seen. Early flyers about the Cacti-Pin state that they were available in eight colors. These may be unmarked or bear an incised mark on the back:

> CACTI-PIN
> Trade Mark
> US Pat Off
> FRANKOMA

FRANKOMA JEWELRY
Lady's Bo and Bolo Ties.

TURTLE PAPER WEIGHT
4 1/2" No. 170
I-1971-SA
Glaze-Woodland Moss (Post-1970)

ADVERTISING & SPECIALS

BONNET WOMAN MEDALLION
2 1/4"   Pacing Leopard Logo
Circa 1936-37   Glaze-Ivory
TEXAS COWBOY MEDALLION
2"   Pacing Leopard Logo
Dated 1936   Glaze-Osage Brown
WOMAN MEDALLION
1 3/4"   Pacing Leopard Logo
Circa 1936-37   Glaze-Ivory

50TH ANNIVERSARY BELL
(OWEN & OPEL) 1 3/4"
Dated 1913-1963
Glaze-Desert Gold, Red Clay
MINIATURE CUP 1 1/2"
Mark reads: PTA '45
Glaze-Prairie Green, Ada Clay
Grace Lee was active in the PTA and
made these as favors.
WEDDING BELLS 1 3/4"
Left: Dated 1954
Glaze-White Sand, Ada Clay
Right: Dated 1962
Glaze-White Sand, Red Clay
Were given as mementoes at the
wedding receptions of Donna and
Joniece. Each bear appropriate
names and wedding dates.

"IOWA SUNSHINE" JUG
6 1/2"
Circa Early '50s
Glaze-Prairie Green, Ada Clay
"TEXAS CENTENNIAL 1936"
THREE CUP JUG 5"
Pacing Leopard Logo
Glaze-Ivory

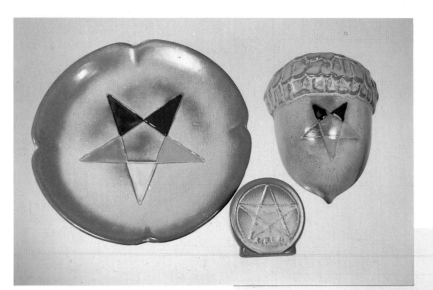

OKLAHOMA EASTERN STAR LOGO
Plainsman 7" Plate, Acorn Wall Pocket and modified Wagon Wheels Individual Sugar. Glaze- Desert Gold, Ada Clay

"UNCLE SLUG" JUG   2 1/4"
No. 10
I-1942   D-1953   Glaze-Osage Brown
The "UNCLE SLUG" (fictitious name) Jug was in production for eleven years. Mold number was changed in 1950 to 561.
"POE'S LIQUORS"   Backside reads: FT. SMITH
Circa 1942   Glaze-Osage Brown

"TULSARAMA!" ASHTRAY
7 3/4"
Circa 1957   Glaze-Desert Gold, Red Clay

LAMP OF KNOWLEDGE CANDLEHOLDER
Glaze-Prairie Green, Red Clay
LAMP OF KNOWLEDGE TRAY
5 1/2"
Glaze-White Sand, Red Clay
Made for "ALPHA SIGMA TAU," an honorary social sorority.

"ANN'S BAKERY & COFFEE SHOP"
(Tulsa) **ASHTRAY** 4"
Circa Late '50s Glaze-White Sand,
Red Clay
"ROMAN NOSE STATE PARK"
ASHTRAY 7"
Opposite side reads: "WATONGA,
OK"

JOHN FRANK APPRECIATION
BOWLS 7 1/2"
Circa 1960s Glaze-White Sand,
Brown Satin, Red Clay
John Frank designed, with his personal signature to be given away
to choice customers as a gesture of
"thanks".

FRANKOMA POTTERY AWARD - CREATIVE
CERAMICS 7"
Circa Late '60s & Early '70s
Glaze-Desert Gold, Prairie Green, Red Clay
Prize trophy given at art shows for pottery piece with most
originality. Originally made for the State Fair at San Antonio, Texas.

"TERPSICHORE" WALL PLAQUE 5"
Circa 1950 Glaze-Desert Gold, Ada Clay
Made for the members of the Drama Club at the University
of Oklahoma in Norman.

51

PRESBYTERIAN TOKEN
1 3/4"
Designed by John Frank in 1967 for the National Meeting of Presbyterian Women. The backside reads: "DARE TO BE NO LONGER STRANGERS".

LORD'S SUPPER CHALICE
8"
Circa Early '70s
Joniece modeled this from a hand carved goblet.
Made for a church as part of a Communion Set.

OIL DERRICK SALT & PEPPER
3"
Glaze-Desert Gold, Red Clay
Produced in 1957 for Oklahoma's Semicentennial Celebration and sold as souvenirs.

TURNER TURNPIKE SALT & PEPPER 3 1/2"
Glaze-Prairie Green, Red Clay
Made to celebrate the opening of Oklahoma's first turnpike on May 16, 1953. Were given away at the Toll Gate and later sold at the Midway Gift Shop.

HORSESHOE SALT & PEPPER
3"
Glaze-White Sand, Red Clay
Another 1957 Oklahoma Semicentennial souvenir.

"BILL WHITE CHEVROLET CO." ASHTRAY   L-7 1/2"
Circa 1960s
Glaze-White Sand, Red Clay

ORCHID MUG 1982
No. C1 Glaze-Prairie Green
Third Orchid mug in a series beginning in 1980.
Made for Gary Schaum, Tulsa, Oklahoma.
FRANKOMA'S 50TH ANNIVERSARY MUG (1983) No. C2
Joniece only made a few for the employees and a few friends.
THE BLOSSOM SHOP MUG 1987
Glaze-Mountain Haze
Made for Jim Waite, Farmer City, Illinois.

THE BRAILLE SYSTEM PLATE   9"
Designed by Joniece Frank in 1977 for the Wessian Company.
Marked: "LIMITED EDITION/500"
Only 500 were made and all were supposed to be glazed in White Sand. This one is in Rubbed Bisque!

CONESTOGA WAGON PLATE   8 1/2"
Glaze-Very Pale Blue
Ideas and sketches originating with Ken Mettin as a fund raiser for the Tulsa Association of Retarded Citizens were worked into a design in clay by John Frank in 1971.
Back Reads: "WE BELIEVE THAT DIGNITY, HAPPINESS AND SELF WORTH ARE THE GOALS OF ALL MENTALLY RETARDED PERSONS." Production number was 2,000. Each plate is numbered.

FRANKOMA'S 50TH ANNIVERSARY TRAY   3 3/4"
Glaze-Prairie Green (Post-1970), Red Clay
Joniece designed this tray in 1983 to commemorate Frankoma's 50th Anniversary. These were given away.

53

CALIFORNIA POTTERY SHOW 1987
A special order by Susan Cox, sold at the show.

"THE ABC'S OF LIFE" ORNAMENT 3 1/2"
This was a Christmas gift with purchase at a Tulsa Shopping Mall in 1987.

TEXAS STATE PLATE   Glaze-Coffee
Reads: "TEXAS THE LONE STAR STATE"
Back of Plate gives pertinent information on Texas.
"THE SOONER STATE"   Glaze-Desert Gold, Red Clay
Reads: "OKLAHOMA 46TH STATE 1907"
Back of the Plate tells of the capitol, state bird, tree, etc.

"OKLAHOMA LAND RUN" PLATE
Glaze-Peach
Reads: "1889 - CENTENNIAL - 1989"
Back gives information about the Oklahoma Land Run.
"LIMITED EDITION"

"1933 - FRANKOMA - 1993"
"60TH ANNIVERSARY"
Joniece Frank captured some major symbols that represent the sixty-year history of Frankoma.

DINNER & KITCHENWARE

Through the years Frankoma has offered three styles of Canister Sets. Each set consisted of a Flour, Sugar, Coffee and Tea canister. A Grease canister was also available.

MAYAN-AZTEC No. 24F, 24S, 24C, 24T, 24G
I-1968   D-1975   Glaze-Woodland Moss (Pre-1970)
RINGED No. 26F, 26S, 26C, 26T, 26G
I-1968-SA   Glaze-Autumn Yellow
SCALLOPED BASE No. 25F, 25S, 25C, 25T, 25G
I-1960   D-1974   Glaze-Prairie Green, (Pre-1970)
Each handle reads: FLOUR, SUGAR, COFFEE, TEA for the appropriate jar. In 1968 these handles were changed to those of the Ringed canister.

3-QUART COOKIE JAR W/ SWAN LID H-10"   No. 99
I-1942 Only   Glaze-Prairie Green
Notice the rim of the lid is silver overlaid. The lid was also available with a miniature horse or plain knob handle.

GUERNSEY PITCHER   No. 93
I-1934   D-1965
Glaze-Iridescent Black 5 1/2"
Mark: 1934-35
Glaze-Prairie Green   6 1/2"
Mark: 1940s
MINIATURE PITCHER
2"   No. 550
I-1940   D-1964
Glaze-Desert Gold, Ada Clay
GUERNSEY CREAMER
3 1/2"   No. 93A
I-1940-42
Glaze-Desert Gold, Ada Clay
LARGE GUERNSEY PITCHER W/O LID   7"
Mark: Pacing Leopard
Glaze-Ivory
Reads: "GOLDEN GUERNSEY"
Bottom Reads: "MERRY CHRISTMAS - MEADOW LODGE FARMS"

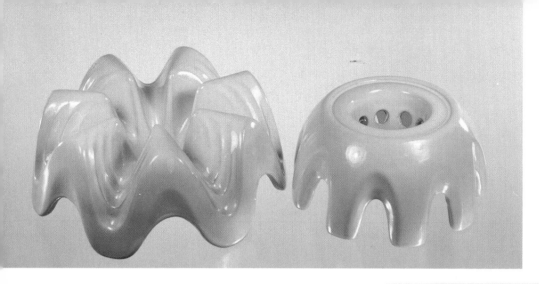

WARMER   8"   No. WA1
I-1974   SA   Glaze-White Sand
WARMER   6"   No. WA3
I-1982   SA   Glaze-White Sand

CONDIMENT JUGS   4 1/2"
Glaze-Desert Gold (Pre-1970)
Circa 1960s   No. X-1 MUSTARD, X-2 RELISH, X-3 VINEGAR, X-4 CATSUP, X-5 OIL, X-6 BAR-B-Q

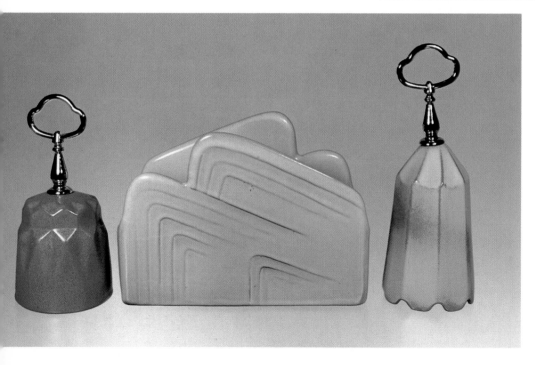

TABLE BELL   6"   No. 817
I-1982   D-1992
Glaze-Brown Satin (Post-1970)
NAPKIN HOLDER
5"   No. 264
I-1983   D-1991
Glaze-White Sand
TABLE BELL   7"   No. 815
I-1980   D-1992
Glaze-Desert Gold (Post-1970)

ELEPHANT SALT & PEPPER
3" No. 160H
I-1942 Only   Glaze-Prairie Green
BULL SALT & PEPPER   2"
No. 166H
I-1942 Only   Glaze-Silver Sage
PUMA SALT & PEPPER
3" No. 165H
I-1942   D-1957   Glaze-White
Sand, Redbud

WAGON WHEEL SHAKER
No. 94H
I-1942   Since 1988-Special Or-
der Only Glaze-Bone
WESTWIND SHAKER No. 6H
I-1962-SA
Glaze-Desert Gold (Post-1970)
**MAYAN AZTEC SMALL
SHAKER**   No. 7HS
I-1948-SA   Glaze-Prairie Green
**MAYAN AZTEC LARGE
SHAKER**   No. 24H
I-1949   D-1975
Glaze-Desert Gold, Ada Clay
PLAINSMAN SMALL SHAKER
No. 5HS (5H after 1960)
I-1948-SA
Glaze-Brown Satin (Pre-1970)
PLAINSMAN LARGE SHAKER
No. 5H
I-1949   D-1953   Glaze-Redbud
LAZYBONES SALT & PEPPER
No. 4H
I-1953   D-1991
Glaze-Desert Gold, Ada Clay

BARREL SALT & PEPPER
No. 97H
I-1950 D-1961
Glaze-Prairie Green, Ada Clay
GUERNSEY SALT & PEPPER
No. 93H
I-1942 Only   Glaze-Ivory
SNAIL SHAKER No. 558H
I-1942 D-1949
Glaze-Prairie Green, Ada Clay
MILK CAN SALT & PEPPER
No. MC/SP
I-1988-SA   Glaze-Robin Egg Blue
**WHEAT SHOCK SALT & PEP-
PER** No. 48H
I-1951-57   Reissued 1981-83
Glaze-Prairie Green, Ada Clay

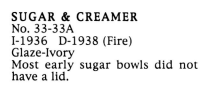

SUGAR & CREAMER
No. 33-33A
I-1936 D-1938 (Fire)
Glaze-Ivory
Most early sugar bowls did not
have a lid.

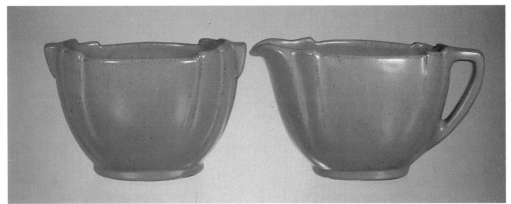

SUGAR & CREAMER
No. 92A-92B
I-1942 Only Glaze-Onyx Black

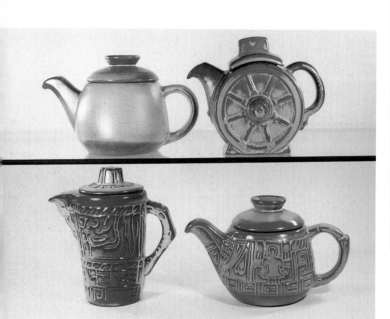

SUGAR W/LID   No. 92A
I-1942 Only Glaze-Silver Sage
Having a lid is very unusual.
Rare!

WESTWIND 2-CUP TEAPOT
No. 6J
I-1966-SA
Glaze-Desert Gold (Pre-1970)
WAGON WHEELS 2-CUP TEA-POT   No. 94J
I-1948   D-1988
Glaze-Prairie Green, Ada Clay
MAYAN AZTEC 2-CUP TEAPOT
No. 7J
I-1948   D-1970
Glaze-Desert Gold (Pre-1970)
MAYAN AZTEC 2-CUP TEAPOT
No. 7J
I-1971-SA   Glaze-Prairie Green

CRACKER TRAY 6" x 6 3/4"
Circa 1942   Glaze-Royal Blue
A very rare piece! Notice the
grooves in the bottom of the tray,
to hold the crackers upright.

**MAYAN AZTEC INDIVIDUAL
BAKER** No. 7U
I-1949 D-1972
Glaze-Prairie Green, Ada Clay
BARREL INDIVIDUAL BAKER
No. 97U
I-1957 D-1961
Glaze-Woodland Moss (Pre-1970)
**WAGON WHEELS INDIVIDUAL
BAKER** No. 94U
I-1948 D-1953
Glaze-Desert Gold, Ada Clay
**LAZYBONES INDIVIDUAL
BAKER** No. 4XU
I-1953 D-1958 Glaze-Clay Blue
**PLAINSMAN INDIVIDUAL
BAKER** 16 OZ. No. 5U
I-1948 D-1953
Glaze-Prairie Green, Ada Clay

TEAPOT 8-CUP No. 92
I-1942 Only Glaze-Prairie Green
TEACUP 6 OZ. No. 92C
I-1942 Only Glaze-Dusty Rose

LARGE TEA PITCHER No. 94
I-1934 D-1938 (fire)
Glaze-Iridescent Black/Ivory
TEACUPS No. 95
I-1934 D-1938 (fire)
Glaze-Iridescent Black/Ivory
Notice the inside of the cups and
teapot are glazed Ivory.

59

ICED TEA PITCHER (PINCHED LIP) No. 87
I-1936   D-1938 (Fire)   Glaze-Prairie Green
BATTER PITCHER 50 OZ. No. 91
I-1936   D-1942   Glaze-Osage Brown
A smaller pitcher for syrup was also available.

BARREL PITCHER HALF-GALLON   No. 97D
I-1950   D-1961   Glaze-Prairie Green
BARREL MUG 14 OZ.   No. 97M
I-1950   D-1961   Glaze-Prairie Green

MAYAN AZTEC PITCHER
8"   No. 7D
Pacing Leopard Logo
I-1936-SA
Glaze-Desert Gold, Ada Clay
MAYAN AZTEC STEINS
5 1/4"   No. 7M
Pacing Leopard Logo
I-1936-SA
Glaze-Desert Gold, Ada Clay

ONE-HALF GALLON PITCHER
8 3/4"
Pacing Leopard Logo
I-1936-SA
Glaze-Prairie Green, Ada Clay
MUGS 10 OZ. No. 81
Pacing Leopard Logo
I-1936-37
Glaze-Prairie Green, Ada Clay

JUICE JUG W/STOPPER 1 QT.
No. 90
I-1936 D-1942 Glaze-Royal
Blue
**REFRIGERATOR JUG W/STOP-
PER** 1 1/2 QT. No. 88
I-1936 D-1958 Glaze-Ivory

BABY MUGS 3" No. 48
I-1934 D-1942
Glazes: Dusty Rose, Old Gold, Ivory,
Osage Brown, Prairie Green and
Sky Blue.

**CHILD'S "MOUSE" PLATE &
MUG** No. 257
I-1983   D-1991   Glaze-Robin
Egg Blue

**LAZYBONES 10" DINNER
PLATE** No. 4F
**LAZYBONES 7 OZ. CUP & SAU-
CER** No. 4C & 4E
LAZYBONES SUGAR W/LID
No. 4B
I-1953   D-1991   Glaze-Sun-
flower Yellow
The Lazybones Dinnerware was in
production from 1953 to 1991.

WAGONWHEEL TRIVET
No. 94TR
I-1957 Only   Glaze-Prairie
Green, Red Clay
LAZYBONES TRIVET No. 4TR
I-1957 Only   Glaze-Desert Gold,
Red Clay
Of all the trivets Frankoma has pro-
duced, these two are the hardest
to find.

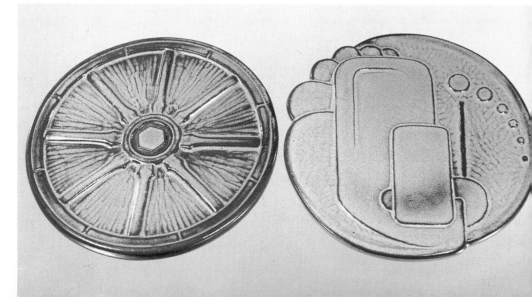

**WAGON WHEELS TEAPOT
6-CUP** No. 94T
I-1942 D-1976
Glaze-Prairie Green, Ada Clay
**WAGON WHEELS TEAPOT
2-CUP** No. 94J
I-1948 D-1988
Glaze-Prairie Green, Ada Clay

WAGON WHEEL CREAMER
No. 94A
**WAGON WHEEL SALT & PEP-
PER** No. 94H
WAGON WHEEL SUGAR
No. 94B
I-1942 D-1988 Glaze-Prairie
Green, Ada Clay
Wagon Wheels Dinnerware was
first introduced in 1942. Addi-
tional pieces have been added and
dropped from the line through the
years. In 1988 the pattern was dis-
continued and only replacement
pieces have been available since.

**WAGON WHEEL CUP 5 OZ. &
SAUCER** No. 94C & 94E
WAGON WHEEL 10" PLATE
No. 94FL
**WAGON WHEEL DESSERT
BOWL 6 OZ.** No. 94XO
I-1942 D-1988 Glaze-Prairie
Green, Ada Clay

WAGON WHEEL 1 QT. VEGETABLE BOWL No. 94N
WAGON WHEEL DEEP PLATTER 13"   No. 94Q
I-1942   D-1988   Glaze-Prairie Green, Ada Clay

FRANKOMA'S DINNERWARE TODAY

CHRISTMAS CARDS

The first limited edition series Frankoma produced, without realizing it, was its annual Christmas Cards.

Because of World War II our country was experiencing some very difficult times in 1944 and everyone was affected by it. It was because of this that John and Grace Lee decided, since their least valuable commodities were clay and time, to make and send ceramic Christmas Cards to their friends that Christmas season instead of the usual greeting cards.

The miniature pitcher, No. 556, that had been a part of Frankoma's general stock since 1942, was chosen for the first Frankoma ceramic Christmas card. The little pitcher was incised on the bottom "THE FRANKS XMAS 1944". Every card that has ever been made can be identified by three marks (in no particular order): 1) "XMAS" if room would not permit "CHRISTMAS", 2) "THE FRANKS", and 3) "YEAR".

After the Christmas season, the Christmas message was removed and the small pitcher again became a part of the general stock. This became the rule for most of the Christmas Cards until 1969. Beginning in 1969, the mold was destroyed immediately after the cards were mailed. They were not put into the general stock.

Supplies and personnel were limited during and just after the war, therefore no cards were made and sent out during the years of 1945 and 1946.

Because of the popularity of the first ceramic Christmas Card, John and Grace Lee chose to send another one in 1947 and did so every year thereafter as long as John Frank was alive. Joniece continued to carry on this tradition through 1982. No cards have been sent with the Frankoma name since, with the exception of 1987 and 1988. Grace Lee and A. Milton Smith shared their Christmas greeting, these two years, with Joniece and Frankoma.

Initially the ceramic Christmas Card was made to send to friends of the Frank family, but as Frankoma grew and dealerships were added, these dealers became a part of the annual Frankoma Christmas Card list. The cards were never made to sell, therefore they are not shown in any of the catalogs. Quantities produced were never recorded.

These cards have been found in a variety of colors up to 1969, but since 1969 have always been glazed in White Sand with one exception, the 1972 card was glazed in Prairie Green, Frankoma's all time best selling color.

Top:				Bottom:		
1944	No. 556	Glaze-Prairie Green		1950		Glaze-Desert Gold
1947	No. 510	Glaze-Prairie Green		1951	No. 552	Glaze-Redbud
1948	No. 560	Glaze-Prairie Green		1952	No. 557	Glaze-Sorghum Brown
1949	No. 551	Glaze-Desert Gold		1953	No. 562	Glaze-Clay Blue
				1954	No. 511	Glaze-Clay Blue

Top:	1955	No. 512	Glaze-Black
	1956	No. 513	Glaze-Black
	1957	No. 463	Glaze-Desert Gold
	1958		Glaze-Brown Satin
	1959	No. 467	Glaze-Prairie Green
Center:			
	1960	No. 468	Glaze-Woodland Moss
	1961	No. 470	Glaze-Woodland Moss
	1962	No. 472	Glaze-Desert Gold
	1963	No. 476	Glaze-Brown Satin
Bottom:			
	1964	No. 477	Glaze-Peach Glow
	1965	No. 481	Glaze-Woodland Moss
	1966	No. 514	Glaze-Prairie Green
	1967		Glaze-Peach Glow
	1968		Glaze-Prairie Green

Top:	1969	THE MOON LANDING
	1970	A PRAYER FOR PEACE
	1971	THANK YOU FROM GRACE LEE & JOHN FRANK
	1972	THREE FRANK VASES
	1973	SPIRAL TO HEAVEN
Center:		
	1974	BUTTERFLY
	1975	YEAR OF THE POTTER
	1976	THE BICENTENNIAL
	1977	BOOK WITH RESTING HANDS
Bottom:		
	1978	THE ARTIST'S VASE AND PALETTE
	1979	CHRISTMAS CANDLE AND BELLS
	1980	YELLOW RIBBON
	1981	SATURN (Grace Lee's design)
	1982	OKLAHOMA'S DIAMOND JUBILEE (Grace Lee's design)

GRACE LEE & A. MILTON SMITH CHRISTMAS CARDS
In February of 1975, Grace Lee and Dr. A. Milton Smith were married. Grace Lee continued the tradition of designing and giving ceramic Christmas Cards each year until 1989 with one exception. None were given in 1983, the year of the fire. All are glazed in White Sand with the exception of 1978 when the cards were glazed in Coffee.

Top: 1975 **BIRD IN HAND**
       1976 **THE BICENTENNIAL**
       1977 **ANGEL BEARING GOOD TIDINGS**
       1978 **JESUS IN THE MANGER**
       1979 **YEAR OF THE CHILD**
Middle:
       1980 **DOVE IN FLIGHT**
       1981 **SATURN**
       1982 **OKLAHOMA'S DIAMOND JUBILEE**
       1983 **NONE**
       1984 **BETHLEHEM STAR**
Bottom:
       1985 **MADONNA**
       1986 **STATUE OF LIBERTY TORCH**
       1987 **WRITING OF CONSTITUTION BICENTENNIAL**
       1988 **BUTTERFLY**
       1989 **CHRISTMAS TREE ORNAMENT**

CHRISTMAS PLATES

In the early sixties, John Frank, who was usually a few steps ahead of others, saw a need for collector's items. He realized that only a few countries, America not included, were producing plates for collectors. The prospects for a new product led him to get involved, inspiring his decision to create an annual plate.

He decided to design a series of plates around the most important season of the year, Christmas. Since Christmas originated with God giving a gift, a Savior to the world, he knew that the message of his plates must point to that gift...Jesus. Therefore, each plate bears a biblical message in picture and in word.

In 1965, Frankoma's first Christmas Plate was released and each year thereafter a new plate has been introduced. Each 8 1/2" plate is a treasure of art, glazed in semi-translucent Della Robia white. Each master mold through 1973 was signed by John Frank, and since then all have been signed by Joniece Frank. The plates are not numbered. All plates are copyrighted and no seconds are sold.

POLITICAL MUGS

John Frank designed a five ounce Elephant Mug in 1968, for what was originally to be a fundraiser for the National Republican Womens' Club however, it soon turned into another collector's series. The Elephant Mug became a stock item thereafter. Later, Joniece designed the five ounce Donkey Mug to represent the Democratic Party. It was first available in 1975, and it also became a stock collector's item.

Every inaugural year the mug bears the names of the President and Vice-President, on either the Elephant or Donkey, depending on the political party winning office. Each year a new color is chosen and the date is changed. Each mug has the date on the right side and the party abbreviation (GOP or DEM) on the other side. Each mug is approximately 4" high and all are glazed white inside. No seconds are available. None of the mugs are numbered.

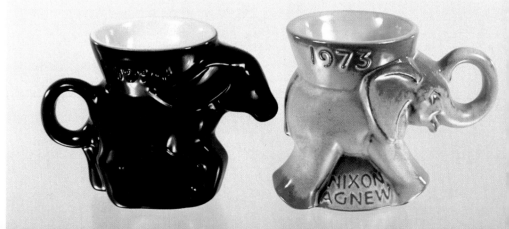

1994 **DONKEY MUG**   Cobalt Blue,
1973 **NIXON-AGNEW**   Desert Gold

1974 "NIXON-FORD" Glaze-Coffee
Very rare! It was not an inaugural year. Less than 500 were made for the National Republican Womens' Club that year.

1968 **ELEPHANT** Glaze-White
1969 **ELEPHANT** Glaze-Flame Marked: "NIXON-AGNEW"
1970 **ELEPHANT** Glaze-Blue
1971 **ELEPHANT** Glaze-Black
1972 **ELEPHANT** Glaze-Prairie Green
1973 **ELEPHANT** Glaze-Desert Gold Marked: "NIXON-AGNEW"
1974 **ELEPHANT** Glaze-Coffee
1975 **ELEPHANT & DONKEY** Glaze-Autumn Yellow
1976 **ELEPHANT & DONKEY** Glaze-Centennial Red
1977 **ELEPHANT & DONKEY** Glaze-Dusty Rose Donkey Marked: "CARTER-MONDALE"
1978 **ELEPHANT & DONKEY** Glaze-Woodland Moss
1979 **ELEPHANT & DONKEY** Glaze-Brown Satin
1980 **ELEPHANT & DONKEY** Glaze-Terra Cotta
1981 **ELEPHANT & DONKEY** Glaze-Celery Green

Elephant Marked: "REAGAN-BUSH"
1982 **ELEPHANT & DONKEY** Glaze-Robin Egg Blue
1983 **ELEPHANT & DONKEY** Glaze-Wisteria
1984 **ELEPHANT & DONKEY** Glaze-Mulberry
1985 **ELEPHANT & DONKEY** Glaze-Navy Blue Elephant Marked: "REAGAN-BUSH"
1986 **ELEPHANT & DONKEY** Glaze-Mountain Haze
1987 **ELEPHANT & DONKEY** Glaze-Lemon
1988 **ELEPHANT & DONKEY** Glaze-Black Onyx
1989 **ELEPHANT & DONKEY** Glaze-Peach Elephant Marked: "REAGAN-BUSH"
1990 **ELEPHANT & DONKEY** Glaze-Teal Green
1991 **ELEPHANT & DONKEY** Glaze-Mottled Ivory
1992 **ELEPHANT & DONKEY** Glaze-Mauve
1993 **ELEPHANT & DONKEY** Glaze-Forest Green Donkey Marked: "CLINTON-GORE"
1994 **ELEPHANT & DONKEY** Glaze-Cobalt Blue

LIMITED EDITION VASES
1969 - 1983

In 1969, John Frank began a collector's series of bottle vases. Each year a newly designed vase was offered and a limited quantity of pieces produced. This quantity was always stated in advance in order to protect the collector's investment. After the limited quantity was produced, the master mold was destroyed. Each vase was numbered and signed by the artist. Each new design had a different colored glaze. The series ended in 1983, Frankoma's 50th Anniversary.

V-1 15" Prairie Green/Black base 4,000
V-2 12" Turquoise Blue 10,000
V-3 12" Red and Black 7,500
V-4 12" Black and Terra Cotta 5,000
V-5 13" Flame, White & Black base 5,000
V-6 13" Celadon & Black base 4,000
V-7 13" Desert Gold, Coffee base & stopper 3,500
V-8 13" Red & White, Red stopper 3,500
V-9 13" White, Black base & stopper 3,000
V-10-B 11 1/2" Morning Glory Blue & White
V-10-C Same vase in Coffee. First time the vases were offered in two colors. A total of 3,000 impressions were made.
V-11-C 11 1/2" Coffee & White, Companion to V-10
V-11-B Same Vase in Morning Glory Blue Total of 3,000 impressions
V-12 13" Black w/Terra Cotta 3,000
V-13 13" Black w/Terra Cotta 3,000 Companion to V-12
V-14 11" Flame & Black 3,000 Because of popular demand, Frankoma reissued this vase marked "Second Edition" on the bottom; it was not numbered. Mold number V14-2.

V-15 13" Prairie Green 3,000 Impressions Last in series.

WILDLIFE PLATE SERIES
1972 - 1979

In 1972, Frankoma began production of this series of plates for the Oklahoma Wildlife Federation. Each year, one thousand plates were produced depicting a different endangered species.

The majority of these were given to new and active members of the Wildlife Federation, given out as door prizes, and so on at various functions. Some were sold to the general public. All proceeds went to funding the conservation efforts of the Wildlife Federation.

Because of a fire at the Federation offices and rebuilding expenses, no plate was produced in 1976.

All are glazed in Prairie Green.

TEENAGERS OF THE BIBLE
1972 - 1982

Each 7" plate in this series of ten represents the life of a biblical youth. They are glazed in Desert Gold. However, John Frank glazed several of the first plates in White Sand and presented them to each member of a big "Youth For Christ" rally in December, 1972.

There is not a "Teenager Of The Bible" plate dated 1973. All master molds were destroyed each year on Christmas Eve.

1979 "BUFFALO" Last plate of the series.

1972 "BOBWHITE QUAIL"
1973 "WHITE-TAILED DEER"
1974 "PRAIRIE CHICKEN"
1975 "LARGEMOUTH BASS"
1977 "GRAY SQUIRREL"
1978 "WILD TURKEY"
1979 "BUFFALO" (Pictured)

1976 "DORCAS THE SEAMSTRESS"
(Fourth in the series)

1972 "JESUS THE CARPENTER"
1974 "DAVID THE MUSICIAN"
1975 "JONATHAN THE ARCHER"
1976 "DORCAS THE SEAMSTRESS"
(Pictured)
1977 "PETER THE FISHERMAN"
1978 "MARTHA THE HOMEMAKER"
1979 "DANIEL THE COURAGEOUS"
1980 "RUTH THE DEVOTED"
1981 "JOSEPH THE DREAMER"
1982 "MARY THE MOTHER"

AMERICAN BICENTENNIAL COM-MEMORATIVE PLATES
1972 - 1976

This series of five plates began in 1972 and ended in 1976, the American Bicentennial year. One plate was issued each year, and its mold was destroyed at the end of that same year. Production quantities were not recorded.

The series covers five important parts, one depicted on each plate, of our early heritage, starting at the beginning of the American Revolution and ending with our independence. The theme of each plate is:

1972	PROVOCATIONS (Pictured)
1973	PATRIOTS-LEADERS
1974	BATTLES FOR INDEPENDENCE
1975	VICTORIES FOR INDEPENDENCE
1976	SYMBOLS OF FREEDOM

An interesting and unique feature of this series is that the signatures of the fifty-six signers of the Declaration are reproduced on the backs of the plates, approximately eleven different names on each plate.

Each plate is White Sand in color, 8 1/2" in diameter and signed by the artist.

1972 **PROVOCATIONS** (First in the series of five)

TOBY MUGS
1976 - 1980

All the mugs were designed by Joniece Frank and were produced in a variety of colors. Each year, beginning in 1976, a different personality was depicted on the six ounce mug. (Dated on the backside.) At the end of the year, the date was removed and the mold became a part of the general stock.

1976 **"UNCLE SAM" MUG**
Glaze-Blue
1977 **"COWBOY" MUG** Glaze-Prairie Green
1978 **"BASEBALL PLAYER" MUG** Glaze-Desert Gold
1979 **"GOLFER" MUG** Glaze-Flame
1980 **"IRISH" MUG** Glaze-Desert Gold

MADONNA PLATES

Grace Lee, designer of these plates, wanted her collector's series to represent the religious symbol of the "Perfect Mother", the Madonna.

Each 8 1/2" plate is artist signed, Roman numeral numbered and finished in beautiful hand stained Rubbed Bisque.

The first two Madonna plates are no longer available, the third and fourth plates may still be purchased from Frankoma.

1977 "THE GRACE MADONNA"
1978 "MADONNA OF LOVE"
1981 "THE ROSE MADONNA"
1986 "THE YOUTHFUL MADONNA" (Pictured)

Tamac Pottery
Perry, Oklahoma
1946-1972

Leonard "Lee" Tate grew up in Perry where his father owned the town's first movie theater and his grandfather the first opera house. Lee's ambition was to have his own business. Working hard to that end, he graduated from the school of business at Oklahoma A & M College at Stillwater in 1942. However, World War II forced him to postpone his plans. He joined and received a commission in the navy.

After a brave and physically demanding long tour in a navy "Scouts & Raiders" team, Lee Tate ended up recuperating in a hospital in New York in 1945. While in New York he met Marjorie Hemke, through mutual friends, who later became his wife.

Marjorie was raised in the East and was an art major, graduating from Brown University in Rhode Island. She also attended several other art schools to enhance her education. During the war she worked as a draftsman for General Electric and as a designer of floor coverings for Congoleum-Nairn.

While working at Congoleum-Nairn in New Jersey, Marjorie met Betty Macauley and they became good friends. Betty's husband Allen was released from the army in 1945. Soon the four became very close friends and partners in the adventure of making pottery.

The decision to start a pottery company in Perry, Oklahoma came about in New York, primarily because the men could not find work there. Marjorie had studied sculpture, modeling and design, Betty had taken a course in ceramics, Allen was a very good mechanic and Lee had a good business education. With these combined talents, they felt sure they could make a go of it. So the die was cast and they all worked hard toward that goal.

Lee and Allen went to Perry in the summer of 1946 and constructed a building addition on the back of Lee's father's garage and furnished it with equipment. This completed their first plant. In September, Lee and his parents met Marjorie and her family in New Orleans, where they were married by her grandfather, a minister. Lee and Marjorie returned to Perry after their honeymoon, and Betty joined the group that fall.

They incorporated the business under the name "TAMAC", which came about by combining a few letters from each couple's last name. Company stock was sold and they were on their way in the pottery business.

The first clay used for making pottery was brought in from Kansas and was light tan in color. This proved to be an undependable and low qual-ity source. They soon found a much better white-bodied clay in Georgia. Its composition made Tamac a more desirable pottery because of its ability to withstand high temperatures during firing. It was also lighter in weight.

Their first glaze, called Butterscotch, was yellow with brown trim. Their second was Avocado, a yellow-green trimmed in darker green. Soon Frosty Pine glaze was added, which was a pine green with a lacy white rim. Next followed Frosty Fudge, a soft brown also rimmed with a lighter lacy glaze. The last color added was Raspberry, a pink with a lacy rim. The Butterscotch glaze was soon eliminated because of quality inconsistencies and continual firing problems. Years later, new owners added a glaze called Honey which was ivory-beige in color.

By 1948 the business had grown so rapidly that they outgrew their first little plant and had to seek more building space at a different location. At that time Oklahoma was promoting industrial growth and diversification by donating free land to qualifying businesses. Tamac took advantage of this promotion and received a good site along Highway 64-77, just south of downtown Perry. By re-issuing stock and borrowing money from relatives and friends, they were able to raise the funds needed to order construction of a 40' x 120' Quonset building and new equipment. The new plant was opened in the summer of 1948.

The business continued to grow very fast. Tours were given daily. Local people were hired and trained by Marjorie and Betty. Good outside salesmen were hard to find; thus Lee became their best salesman. One of their largest accounts was Garfinkle's Department Store in Washington, D.C. Due to Tamac's popularity, lack of money, and the many demands put on them by customers, they all felt great pressure. After starting a family, Betty and Allen Macauley became disenchanted with the pottery business, so the Tates bought out their interest in the company in 1950. The Macauleys returned to the East.

The Tates continued the business for another two years, and although their business continued to grow, they were still plagued with financial problems. This forced them into bankruptcy.

Mrs. Earl Bechtold (Lee's Aunt) purchased Tamac in 1952. Her son Raymond operated the plant successfully for a few years by putting additional pieces into the line. But they also ran into financial difficulties and sold out to Mr. Joe Hladik in the sixties. It was operated by his daughter Lenita Moore and later by her mother Mary.

The new owners experienced the same difficulties many businesses have when freeways and turnpikes reroute the flow of tourists in a different direction. The plant was closed permanently in 1972.

Today Marjorie Tate lives in the state of Virginia, successfully doing what she loves best, painting. Lee passed away in 1987. They, together with the Macauleys, have left us with a beautiful, fascinating china quality pottery to admire and enjoy for many years to come.

Two types of marks were used: The oldest mark was incised and the second was a black ink stamp. Both read: TAMAC Perry, Oklahoma, U.S.A.

Young Marjorie Tate demonstrating the "One-Hander".

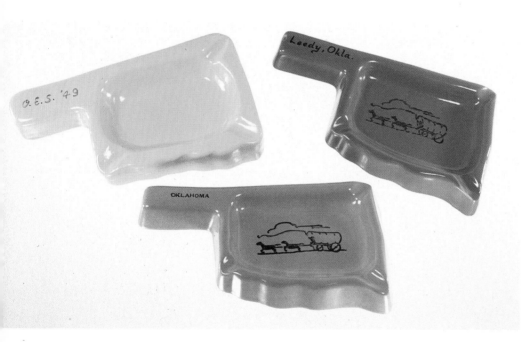

OKLAHOMA ASHTRAYS 7 1/2"
Notice the two on top were used for advertising. Pictured in Butterscotch, Pine and Raspberry without the lacy rim.

ASHTRAYS
The tray on the far right is Frosty Pine, the other two are Frosty Fudge.

74

LARGE VIOLET PLANTER 6"
BIRD 3"
Color-Frosty Fudge
The Bird was made to rest on the rim of the Planter.

LARGE VIOLET PLANTER w/ BIRD
Color-Frosty Fudge
SMALL VIOLET PLANTER 5"
Color-Raspberry

BUD VASE 5 1/2" Frosty Fudge
DISH GARDEN 12" Frosty Pine

LARGE MANTEL PLANTER
18" Raspberry
FREE FORM VASE 4 1/2"
Frosty Pine

WALL VASES 4 3/4" - 5"
Color-Raspberry and Frosty Pine
The vase on far right has a decal fired on and is missing the lacy rim. Inside is glazed pine.

SINGLE and DOUBLE CANDLEHOLDER
Color-Avocado

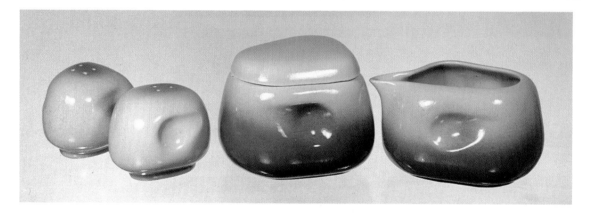

SALT & PEPPER
SUGAR/CREAMER 8 OZ. EACH
Color-Avocado

INDIVIDUAL SUGAR/ CREAMER SET
Color-Raspberry

DECANTER 1 QT. Frosty Pine

TEAPOT/CHOCOLATE POT 24 OZ.
Color-Frosty Fudge

TEAPOT (WITHOUT LID) 6 CUP Color-Frosty Pine
The lid to this teapot is flat, it has no finial.

4 Qt. PITCHER (holds 3 quarts)
2 Qt. PITCHER
JUICE PITCHER 24 OZ.
Color-Avocado

DECANTER GOBLET 6 OZ.
Frosty Pine

TUMBLER 16 OZ. Honey
JUICE TUMBLER 4 OZ. Frosty
Pine

BARBECUE PLATE 15"
BARBECUE CUP 10 OZ.
Color-Avocado
The cup is also used as an Individual Baker.

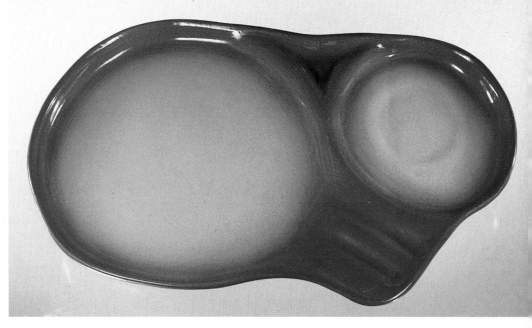

BARBECUE PLATE 15"
Color-Butterscotch
Also called "The One Hander by Tamac". May be found with this mark incised or black ink stamped on the bottom. This "One Hander" has both marks.

This uniquely designed tray is a 9" Dinner Plate and Saucer cast in one piece. It has three grooves for silverware to rest on and a small section for relish.

DINNER PLATE 10"
SALAD PLATE 7"
Color-Avocado

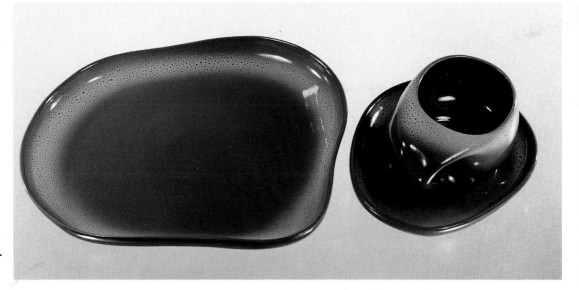

DINNER PLATE 10"
BARBECUE CUP 10 OZ.
BARBECUE SAUCER 7"
Color-Frosty Pine

COFFEE CUP 8 OZ. W/ 6" SAUCER
Frosty Fudge
TEACUP 6 OZ. W/ 6" SAUCER
Frosty Pine
LARGE COFFEE MUG 12 OZ.
Frosty Pine
DEMITASSE CUP W/ SAUCER
Frosty Fudge
The After Dinner Cup holds three tablespoons.

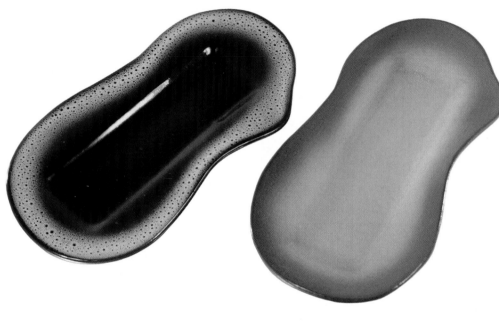

BUTTER DISH 8" Frosty
Fudge & Avocado
Dish did not come with a lid.

**COVERED CASSEROLE 2 QT.
UNDERPLATE/PLATTER** 12"
Color-Frosty Fudge
An 18" Underplate/Platter was also available.

GRAVY BOAT 16 OZ. Frosty Fudge

SERVING BOWLS 1 QT. & 2 QT.   Frosty Fudge
FRUIT BOWL 8 OZ.   Frosty Pine
Tamac also offered a 16 oz. Soup/Cereal Bowl and a Four
Quart Serving Bowl.

DIVIDED RELISH DISH 7"   Avocado & Frosty Fudge

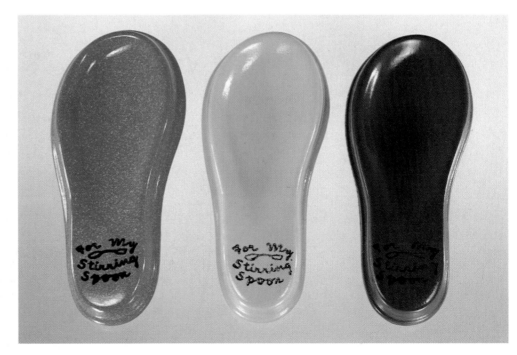

SPOON REST   6"
Colors-Raspberry, Avocado and
Pine, without lacy rim.
Reads: "FOR MY STIRRING SPOON".
Was designed by Leonard's father,
Henry Tate.

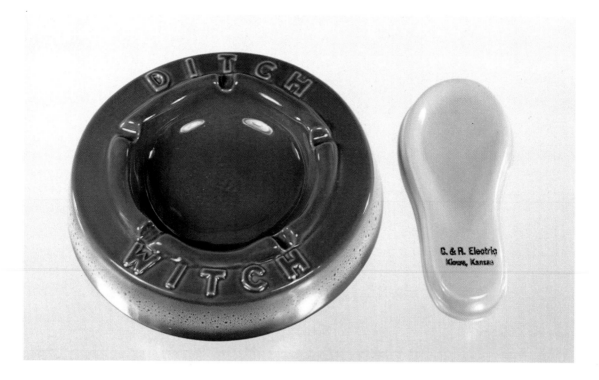

ASHTRAY advertising "DITCH WITCH" Frosty Pine
SPOON REST advertising "C & R ELECTRIC KIOWA, KANSAS" in a pale blue glaze, a departure for Tamac.

The **10" PLATE** advertising "OKEENE FLOUR".

POSTCARD Backside reads:

HOME OF
TAMAC POTTERY
PERRY, OKLAHOMA

Stop and visit our factory and salesroom. Open seven days a week - See pottery made.

Hammat Originals
Tulsa, Oklahoma
1945-1961

Flora Hammat is a fine ceramist and artist. She loves nature and the beautiful shapes of natural things. This love was reflected in her designs. She was an internationally known designer and manufacturer of ceramics.

Flora Mary Eckert was born in Chicago in 1912 and moved to Tulsa with her parents when she was two years old. Her mother died when she was ten. Thereafter, she was raised by her aunt and uncle, who also lived in Tulsa. Flora's aunt inspired her interest in art and especially art pottery. She had studied under Susie Singer, a famous Austrian artist in California.

Flora married Neves Russel Hammat and they had two beautiful daughters, Cinda and Joan. Neves worked for the U.S. Post Office Department in Tulsa. Later, the entire family was involved, to some degree, in the pottery business.

World War II was just starting when Flora began thinking about making art pottery for profit. She and Neves expected him to be called into service, so they began planning a way for her to make a living while he was gone. Feeling the timing was wrong, the pottery idea was shelved temporarily. Flora took some engineering training at Tulsa University and went to work for Service Pipeline Co. and later for Douglas Aircraft Co. As it worked out, Neves' age kept him out of the military, so he remained with the Post Office.

Flora got the pottery bug again in 1945, and decided to quit Douglas and go to U.C.L.A., in California, to study ceramics under Glenn Luken. He was one of the most famous ceramist in the world, primarily because of his unique glazes. Glazes also became Flora's specialty. She worked hard, day and night, learning all she could about clays and glazes. She also learned how to construct kilns. When the course was completed in 1945, she returned to Tulsa to start their pottery business.

Flora and Neves set-up their first plant in their home garage and used the house for storage. Flora built a very small kiln. Their first order was from Seidenbacks, an exclusive Tulsa department store, for $300 worth of ashtrays. In the midst of starting a pottery business and raising a family, Flora went to Kansas University one summer, to study clay mixes.

After working a year in their home more room and larger kilns were needed. Therefore, the Hammat's moved the operation to Flora's mother-in-law's basement. They outgrew this place in about two years, then purchased three acres of land on Tulsa's east edge, along Highway 66. On this site they built a concrete masonry building and four large brick kilns. Retail sales were conducted in this building, and many family meals were served there. In spite of two damaging tornadoes, this plant served their needs for the remaining period they were in business. At its peak, Hammat employed about twenty production people.

Hammat received its clay from California and an additive (volcanic ash) from Kansas. Flora designed the clay mixtures, developed the glazes and made her own molds. Many molds were very complicated, such as shell and leaf forms.

Neves helped in the evenings and weekends as his Post Office job would allow. Flora also received valuable assistance from Cinda and Joan throughout the life of the business. Both girls developed an appreciation for art and are very talented. They each studied art, in some form, while in college.

The phenomenal success of Hammat art pottery was largely due to superior quality and originality. Its flower bowls were designed primarily to inspire the flower lover in the exacting art of flower arranging. It was above criticism in regard to seepage, crazing or excessive weight. The pottery was made with a soft brown mat finish outside and inside colors that complimented and enhanced the beauty of flowers.

All Hammat pottery was hand signed "HAMMAT ORIGINAL" by Flora, incised in the clay or handpainted.

Flora Hammat (center) assisted by daughters Joan (left) and Cinda (right).

Basically, Hammat produced flower arrangement bowls (cache pots), figurines and most unusual ashtrays, including the world famous life size "Hot Foot". Special promotion pieces were made at various times for stores, clubs, etc. Their pottery was offered at trade shows in several large cities each year, and they had a permanent exhibit at the Merchandise Mart in Chicago. Over the years, they offered several different sales catalogs. Hammat sold to many major department stores, such as Neiman Marcus in Dallas. Nationally known flower arrangers used Hammat bowls almost exclusively. Flora was known from coast to coast in garden clubs and womens' clubs, where she was often the featured speaker.

Because Hammat pottery required much hand-work in making, it had to be sold for a premium price. In the 1950s, Japanese imports started taking their toll on American businesses and Hammat was no exception. They could not compete with the lower prices, so they closed their plant in 1961. Flora went to work in real estate sales. Neves was killed in an auto wreck in 1972.

Cinda and Joan finished their educations, married and now have grown children. Flora, now retired, has left us with a pottery having unusual glazes that is truly "original".

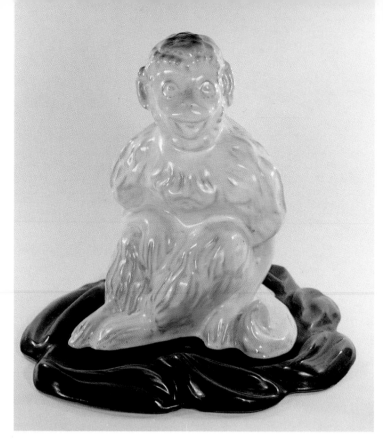

"CHI CHI" MONKEY 10"

FRUIT CENTER PIECE
Diam-15"
Wood Hue finish.

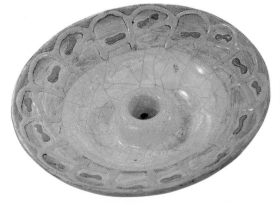

CANDLEHOLDERS

"TICO" CLOWN HEAD 10"

"AKDAR 1953" reads across the lower part of this figurine that stands 6" high.

"CHICO" THE MONKEY 12"

INDIAN MAIDEN WALL MASK 4 1/2"
Made for a special event with the Oklahoma Eastern Star in 1952. Across the neck reads: OES-52. The back is signed "HAMMAT ORIGINAL - TULSA".

RAM 18"

MASK MUGS 3 1/2"
The mugs are hand painted, so are the above pieces. These mugs hold approximately seven ounces each.

"HOT FOOT" ASHTRAY 9"
Underside is dated 1951. Hammat also offered a 5" version called the "WEE HOT FOOT".

This is the famous "Hot Foot" that was featured in a national magazine.

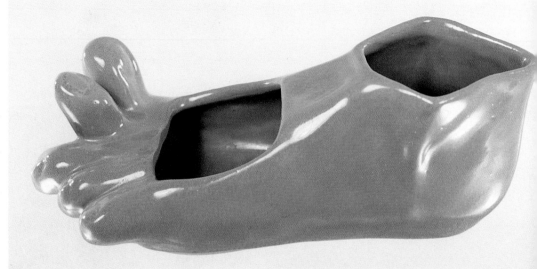

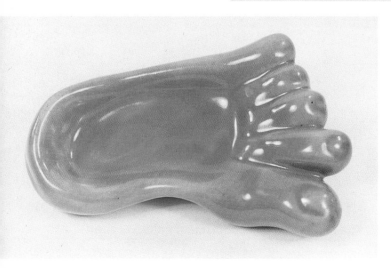

"LITTLE SIDE KICK" ASHTRAY 5"

HAMMAT ORIGINALS STICKER

86

COCONUT MUGS 7 OZ.

NUBIAN BUST ASHTRAY
H-6 1/2"
Made for The Tulsa Club. The bottom reads: "PROPERTY OF THE TULSA CLUB".

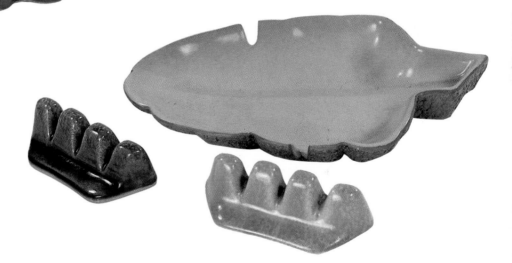

BANANA LEAF ASHTRAY 7"
Flora used a real banana leaf in making this mold. It was available in four sizes up to 17".
CIGARETTE RESTS 4"
Made to lay in the bottom of various trays or bowls.

SEA MYTH ASHTRAYS 6"

WOODLAND ASH BOWL 7"
Was also available in 10".

SHELL CANDLEHOLDERS 6 1/2"

HORN O'PLENTY 13"

COUNCH SHELL BOWL 5"
COUNCH SHELL BOWL 8"

88

WESTERN TUMBLER 4 1/2"

PEDESTAL VASE 9 1/2"

CABBAGE LEAF FOOTED BOWL 9 1/2"
Savoy cabbage leaves were used in making this mold. A larger bowl was also produced.

SPORTSMAN'S DUCK PLATTER 15"
A "Sportsman Series" was specially designed for a world famous New York Sportsmen's store. The series consisted of plates 12 1/2", mugs 16 oz. and footed or flat platters (each in two sizes). Each piece was hand painted.

89

COWBOY HAT HORS d'OEUVRE TRAY   13"
COWBOY HAT MINT TRAY/ ASHTRAY   8"
Bottom reads: "COPYRIGHT 1953 HAMMAT ORIGINALS".
These two pieces were designed and produced for the "Longhorn Room", a restaurant that was located on Tulsa's Eastside at the Western Village Motel. Notice the "WV" branding iron on front of each hat.

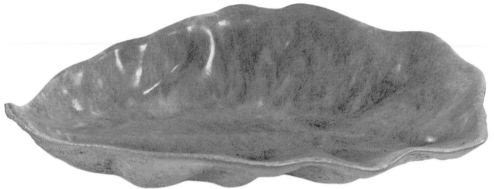

FIDDLE LEAF BOWL   13"

FIDDLE LEAF BOWL   13"

CACHE POT   4 1/2"

CABBAGE LEAF COMPOTE   4 1/2"
The Cabbage Leaf Compote was also available in 6 1/2" and 7 1/2".

FLOWER BOWLS   14"

URN 9"

FOOTED FLOWER BOWL   Diam-8 1/2"

SHELL FAN BOWL 10"
Available in four sizes, from 3" to 18".

ADVANCE DESIGN BOWLS
8" & 12"
These came in various shapes and sizes.

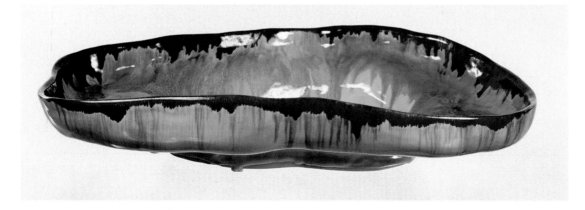

GARDEN CLUB DISH 16"

Winart Pottery
Miami, Oklahoma
1951-1972

This company really had its beginning in the town of Sapulpa in 1951. It was there that David and his wife Clara (Winchell) Arter opened a retail gift shop and wholesale warehouse on Main Street, under the name "WINART". This name was derived from the first three letters of their last names before marriage. Later the business moved to Hobson Street.

Clara was a native Oklahoman, born in the town of Slick, who had worked with the Frank family of Frankoma Pottery, from 1940 until Winart started. She began as a secretary but soon moved into the position of sales manager. David was from Ohio and spent several years in managerial positions for major department stores, after serving in the military during World War II.

Since both of their backgrounds were business related and not in the technical aspects of making pottery, no pottery was manufactured in Sapulpa. David and Clara relied on the American Clay Forming Co. (ACFC) of Tyler, Texas to furnish all their merchandise.

With the exception of mugs, sugar & creamers, tumblers and lazy-susans, all merchandise was art pottery. Winart furnished ACFC molds for all items except art pottery. The pieces made with Winart molds were marked with a capital "W". Natural finished wood serving trays for mugs and lazy-susans were designed and made by Winart. These pieces were ink-stamped "WINART SAPULPA, OKLAHOMA". They offered a four page sales catalog while in Sapulpa.

In 1953, after investigating several cities, the Arters moved their business to the town of Miami in the northeastern part of the state. With the help of the local Chamber of Commerce, they were able to rent a large two story building, with basement, from Northeastern A & M Junior College. Northeastern A & M had used it for student housing.

This new location was along Highway 66 on the north edge of Miami. Many years earlier this building was a noted tavern (filling station, hotel and restaurant, etc.) in a chain of taverns located across the country and owned by Pierce-Pennant Oil Company. Winart occupied a large part of the lower floor of the building, and their salesroom was called the "Serendipity Shop".

For awhile they continued to purchase most items from the firm at Tyler, Texas. Additional pieces were made for Winart by Synar Ceramics of Muskogee, Oklahoma, using Winart molds and specifications. After much deliberation, sweat and tears, the Arters decided to manufacture and sell their own pottery. They used the basement and a new building addition as their manufacturing plant. At this point they put out a new sign, "WINART POTTERY".

David, who was a skilled inventor, mechanic and craftsman, became the mold builder. Clara designed most of the pottery. They purchased their clay from the Sphinks Clay Co. of Paris, Tennessee. The Arters developed and ground their own glazes with help from Mr. F.Q. Mason of Mason Color Chemicals Co., East Liverpool, Ohio. Over the years, David and Clara worked hard to develop a fine line of colorful dinnerware and art pottery. Their motto was "A Thing Of Beauty Is A Joy Forever".

When the Will Rogers Turnpike (extending between Tulsa and Joplin, Missouri—with a toll gate at Miami) was completed in June of 1957, the traffic flow on Highway 66 started to diminish and so did sales. Before long the Arters decided to relocate across town (southeast) to a site along Highway 10 and very close to Highway 66 and the turnpike toll gate. This relocation was done in two stages. They built a new building with a large salesroom, opening in April of 1961. The plant remained at the old tavern site during this stage. An addition was built on behind the salesroom as the second stage and the plant was moved into it. This relocation was completed in February, 1962. The new plant was the most modern in pottery making, with a glassed-in aisle through the plant for public viewing.

At the new site David and Clara continued expanding their pottery lines and marketing areas. They had many catalogs and marketing tools for their pottery salesmen to use. Winart shipped pottery to every state in the Union and to Canada. New retail shop products included quality imports from thirty-four foreign countries.

David became seriously ill in the early 1970s and passed away in 1987. Pottery manufacturing stopped in 1972. The salesroom continued to operate until December of 1981 when the building was sold.

Today, Clara lives in a unique home of which David designed and supervised construction; a home that they shared and enjoyed for many years as they became one of a few successful pottery makers in Oklahoma.

The "Old Tavern" building, Winart's first business location in Miami.

WINART POTTERY SHOWROOM
Miami, Oklahoma

DECANTER 1 QT. 8"
Color-Pink w/brown

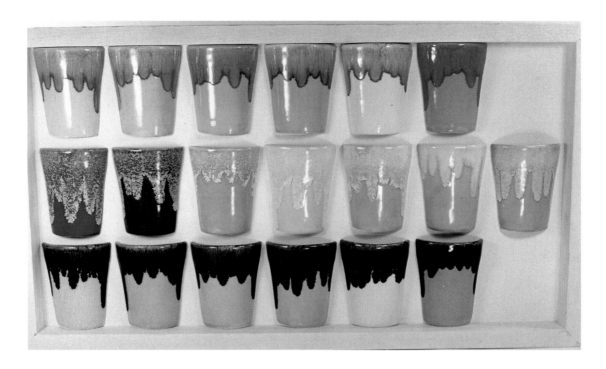

SALESMAN COLOR SAMPLES
Top Row: Gold w/brown, Pink w/brown, Chartreuse w/brown, Blue w/brown, White w/brown, Persimmon w/brown.
Middle: Brown w/frost, Avocado w/frost, Persimmon w/frost, Gold w/frost, Pink w/frost, Blue w/frost, Chartreuse w/frost.
Bottom: Gold w/black, Pink w/black, Blue w/black, Chartreuse w/black, White w/black, Persimmon w/black.

Black w/frost is the only color missing.

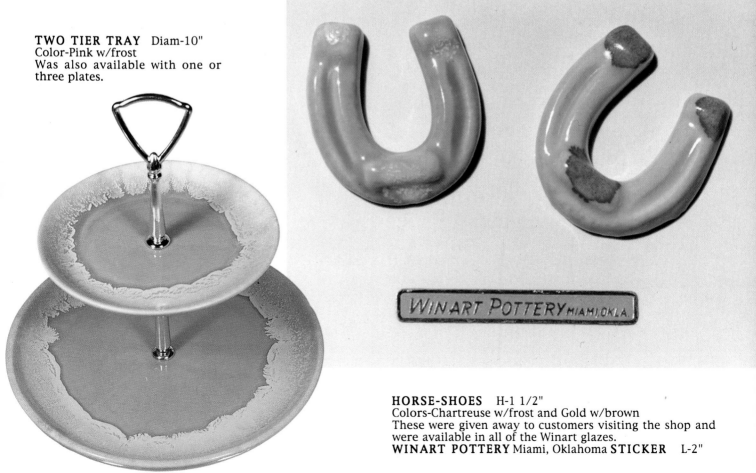

TWO TIER TRAY Diam-10"
Color-Pink w/frost
Was also available with one or three plates.

HORSE-SHOES H-1 1/2"
Colors-Chartreuse w/frost and Gold w/brown
These were given away to customers visiting the shop and were available in all of the Winart glazes.
WINART POTTERY Miami, Oklahoma **STICKER** L-2"

LAZY-SUSAN Diam-16"
Color-Persimmon w/frost

CHIP 'N DIP PLATE
Diam-13"
Color-Persimmon w/frost
Various bowls rest in the center of
the plate for dips, etc. as pictured
in the next photograph.

**CHIP 'N DIP PLATE w/24 OZ.
BOWL**
Color-Persimmon w/frost

96

PITCHER 6" No. 23V
Color-Chartreuse w/brown
PITCHER 2 1/2 QT. 8 1/2"
Color-White w/brown
Also available in 16 oz. and 5
quart, 12".

JUICE TUMBLERS W/CAROUSEL TRAY
Color-Persimmon w/frost

JUICE TUMBLER 7 OZ. No. 27
Color-Persimmon w/frost
A 16-ounce tumbler was also available, No. 28.
JUICE PITCHER 1 1/2 QUART 10" No. 37
Color-Persimmon w/frost
A two-quart pitcher, No. 23J was also produced.

PITCHER 16 OZ. No. 46
Color-Blue w/frost
An eight-ounce pitcher was also available.

COFFEE SERVER 8-CUP H-13"
Color-Persimmon w/frost

PITCHER 2 1/2 QUART No. 203
Color-Brown w/frost

INDIVIDUAL TEAPOT 12 OZ. No. 52
Color-Brown w/frost

TEAPOT 48 OZ. H-7"
Color-Persimmon w/frost
TEAPOT 28 OZ. H-8"
Color-Persimmon w/frost

COFFEE SERVER 9-CUP
12 1/2"
Color-Persimmon w/frost

"ALOHA" MUG 7 OZ. w/CAR-OUSEL TRAY No. 24M
Color-Persimmon w/frost

**MODERNAIR MUG 8 OZ. w/
CAROUSEL TRAY**
No. 23M
Colors: Black w/frost, Persimmon
w/frost, Blue w/frost and Char-
treuse w/frost

MODERNAIR MUG 8 OZ.
No. 23M
TEAPOT 12-CUP No. 23T
Color-Persimmon w/frost

SIP 'N SMOKE TRAY No. 7
TWO-FINGER MUG 8 OZ.
No. 23M
Color-Persimmon w/frost

All six styles of mugs will fit the
tray.

BOWL 48 OZ. 9" No. 23NL
10" BAKER/BOWL No. 49
BOWL 2 QT. No. 23LN
Color-Persimmon w/frost

AU GRATIN DISH 11 1/2"
PEDESTAL MUG 7 OZ.
No. 301
Color-Persimmon w/frost

MODERNAIR MUG 8 OZ.
No. 23M
7" PLATE/SAUCER No. 23E
10" PLATE No. 23F
DESSERT BOWL 8 OZ.
No. 23U
SALAD/SOUP BOWL 12 OZ.
No. 23G
Color-Persimmon w/frost

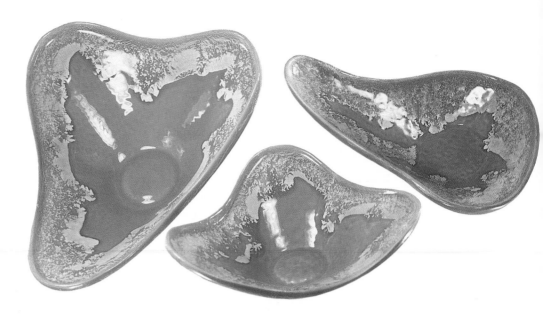

FREE FORM BOWLS   8", 9", and 11"
Color-Persimmon w/frost
A 15" bowl was also available.

SALAD OR PUNCH BOWL 16"
Color-Persimmon w/frost

THREE-GALLON BOWL 16"
Color-Brown w/frost

THREE-LEG CASSEROLE 1 QT.
Color-Chartreuse w/maroon.
This casserole was also available in
two-quart and individual sizes.
PITCHER 52 OZ. No. 23D
Color-Chartreuse w/maroon.
These pieces were produced by
Synar Ceramics for Winart from
Winart molds. The Chartreuse w/
maroon glaze was not one Winart
produced.

CREAMER 8 OZ. No. 27C
Color-Persimmon w/frost
SUGAR 8 OZ. No. 27S
Color-Brown w/frost
Sugar did not come with a lid, it
was open.
CREAMER 8 OZ. No. 23C
Color-Chartreuse w/frost
Winart offered four styles of
creamers.

Left: **PITCHER** 8" No. 23K
Color-Chartreuse w/frost
Front: **SALT & PEPPER** (Ball)
No. 50
Color-Pink w/brown
Back: **SALT & PEPPER** 8"
No. 23H
Color-Persimmon w/frost

Front: **SCALLOPED INDIVIDUAL DISH** 3" No. 10
Color-Persimmon w/frost
TOOTHPICK/MATCH HOLDER
No. 17
Color-Persimmon w/frost
ROUND INDIVIDUAL DISH
3" No. 23Q
Color-Brown w/frost
Back: **BUTTER DISH** 6 1/2"
No. 23Y
Color-Persimmon w/frost
RELISH DISH 7 1/2" No. 35
Color-Pink w/frost

WAGON WHEEL LAZY-SUSAN 24" No. 20
Colors-Brown w/frost, Avocado w/frost, Gold w/brown and Pink w/brown.
The Wagon Wheel Lazy-Susan could be purchased as pictured or purchased with the black wrought iron stand and choice of any coffee service as shown in the next photograph.

WAGON WHEEL LAZY-SUSAN w/STAND AND #238 MODERNAIR COFFEE SERVICE
A Coffee Service consisted of two, four or six mugs (depending on the size tray chosen) and a sugar and creamer.

"MIAMI" ASHTRAY   7 1/2"   No. 14
Color-Persimmon w/frost
Ashtray still has original "Winart" sticker. This ashtray was
available plain (without a design in the bottom) or with an
Indian head encircled by the name "OKLAHOMA".

WIND PROOF ASHTRAY   No. 11
Color-Brown w/frost

FREE FORM ASHTRAY   15"
CIGARETTE LIGHTER (Tooth-
pick Holder)   No. 17
Color-Persimmon w/frost

DRAFT PROOF ASHTRAY   8"   No. 15
Color-Brown w/frost

**TEMPO MUG w/CHRISTMAS
SCENE** No. 22M
**PEDESTAL MUG w/CHRISTMAS
SCENE** No. 301

PLANTER 5 1/2" No. 84
PLANTER 5 1/2" No. 82
Color-Persimmon w/frost

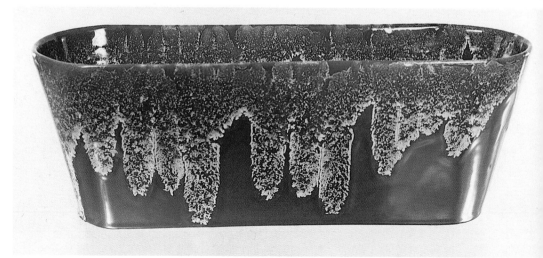

OBLONG PLANTER 15 1/2"
Color-Brown w/frost

SCULPTURED HEAD WALL MASK   18" No. 201
Color-Brown w/frost

PET BOWLS W/WROUGHT IRON STANDS
The Saint Bernard named "Tinker Bell" and "Tommy" the cat, were members of the Arter family.

"TEN LITTLE INDIANS" MUGS
Decals of Charles Banks Wilson's original drawings of "Ten Little Indians" were used on the No. 21M mug and were very colorful.

107

**QUARTERHORSE MUGS w/HORSESHOE HANDLE
TRAY**
Winart offered Angus and Hereford Mugs also. All were on
White.

Sequoyah Pottery
Tahlequah, Oklahoma
Circa 1938-1943

The pottery called "Sequoyah" was made near the old Cherokee Indian Nation Capital, Tahlequah. It was made by members of the Cherokee tribe at the "Sequoyah Orphan Training School", a few miles southwest of town on Highway 62. The school is now known as the "Sequoyah High School".

Symbolic of the progressive nature of the Cherokee Nation, in 1871 they designated fifteen percent of their annual tribal income to the support of orphans and the insane. In that same year, they located the Cherokee Orphan Asylum near the present day Sequoyah High School site. Later in the 1870s, when the tribe bought the Lewis Ross home and farm at Salina, the Asylum moved there. About 1904, the burning of the Salina Asylum required the return of the children back to the original site.

After statehood in 1907, when the tribal governments were abolished among the Five Civilized Tribes (which included the Cherokees), the Federal Government took over a number of old tribal schools and made them United States Indian Schools. The Cherokee Orphan Asylum was sold to the Federal Government in 1914. In 1925 this institution's name was changed to "Sequoyah Orphan Training School". In 1945 it became the "Sequoyah Vocational School" and, since 1964, it has been called "Sequoyah High School".

The development of arts and crafts (such as weaving, basketry and pottery) through the aid of the Indian Arts and Crafts Board of the United States Department of the Interior, starting in 1935, was very successful for the school. All their work could be sold.

The name "Sequoyah" was given to the school and the pottery in tribute to a very famous Cherokee mixed-blood, who's English name was George Guess. In the early 1800s he invented an alphabet, or syllabary, which reduced the Cherokee language to written form. This invention was remarkable because he had never attended school, was illiterate and could not speak English. It took twelve years to perfect, but within a few months after the tribal leaders approved this syllabary, nearly every adult could read and write the language. Books and newspapers were printed in Cherokee by 1828. Sequoyah's people were the best-informed Indians in America, probably better read than the settlers who were trying to take their land. In 1905, the people of Indian Territory (nearly the eastern half of Oklahoma) tried to secure statehood. This new state was to be named "Sequoyah". The plan was not accepted by the Federal Government.

Clay for the Sequoyah pottery came from local sources in tan or red colors. The dates listed in the title represent the earliest and latest dates, we have observed, marked on the pottery. Note that only women's names, the pottery makers, have been found marked on the pieces. This is probably because pottery making–like weaving and basket making–was considered woman's work. Nearby settlement names, such as Welling, are found marked on many pieces. These most likely indicate the home of the potter. Some pieces have a mold number. There were no catalogs. The pottery was only sold locally.

Dr. Bill Ames was hired by the Federal Government in the mid-to-late 1930s to act as Director of Vocational Education. He served in this position for many years and was responsible for developing the arts and crafts program at the school. He was a very talented and highly respected individual. Most of the success of this program was due to his hard work. Dr. Ames died in 1993.

Sequoyah pottery is not only appealing to the eye, but it has a good feel to the touch. It is truly Indian art, of authentic Indian workmanship, at its best. Sequoyah pottery is a very desirable and sought after pottery in Oklahoma, home of the red man.

Sequoyah pottery was glazed in red umber, yellow, white, green and blue. All pottery pictured was made using red clay with a red umber glaze unless otherwise noted.

SEQUOYAH'S HOME 3"
Mk: Lola 1940 Sequoyah

KNEELING POTTERS 6"
One mark each:
Lucy Johnson 1942 Sequoyah
Evelyn O. 1942 Sequoyah

FROG H-2 1/2"
Mk: Olivene Seyaper 1938 Sequoyah

LARGE KNEELING POTTER 8"
Mk: Patty Vineyard 1943
Others as noted above.

ASHTRAY H-2 1/2" Diam-5"
Mk: Emma L. 1940 Sequoyah #35

TURTLE ASHTRAY H-2" L-5 1/2"
Mk: Evelyn Van. 1939 Sequoyah #1

VASE 4 3/4"
Mk: Lucille Works 1939 Sequoyah #20

VASE 4 1/4"
Mk: M. Lawson Cherokee Co.

FROG PLANTER   H-2 3/4" L-6 1/2"
Mk: Evelyn H. 1939 Sequoyah #2

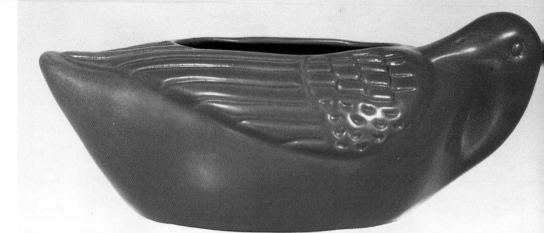

DUCK PLANTER   L-8"
Mk: Melba June 1940 Sequoyah #5

INDIAN POT   H-2 3/4"
Mk: Pauline Harjo Sequoyah
This piece is made with beige clay and is unglazed.

BOWL   Diam-6"
Mk: Mitties Lawson May 27, 1939 Welling Okla

PLANTER H-5 1/2"
Mk: M.L. Welling OK

FROG HANDLE VASE H-3 3/4"
Mk: Cloeta Lowvey 1939 Sequoyah

PLANTER H-2 3/4" L-6"
Mk: Krouse Welling Okla. U.S.A. #10

VASE H-4 1/2"
Mk: Annie 1941 Sequoyah

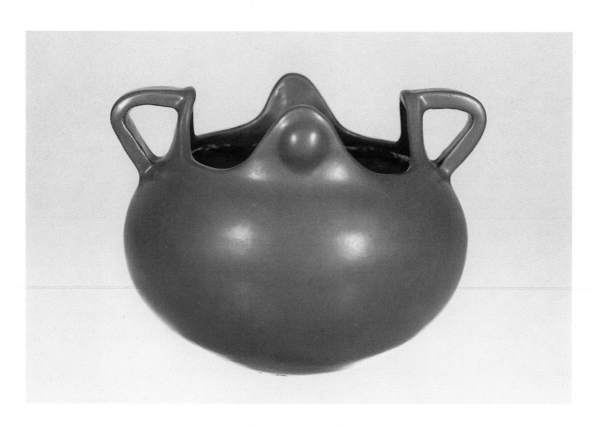

PLANTER H-4 1/4"
Mk: Krouse Welling, Okla

OWL NECK VASE 5 1/2"
Mk: Susie O. 1940 Sequoyah #32

URN 10"
Mk: Levide Going 1938 Sequoyah
Is hand built and very heavy. Brown glaze.

THUNDERBIRD PITCHERS H-3 1/2"
Left Mk: Ruby P. Sequoyah
Center: Geneva Adair Sequoyah #22
Clay is beige with green glaze. Thunderbird is painted black.
Right: Bessie Buster Sequoyah #22
Clay is beige with yellow glaze.

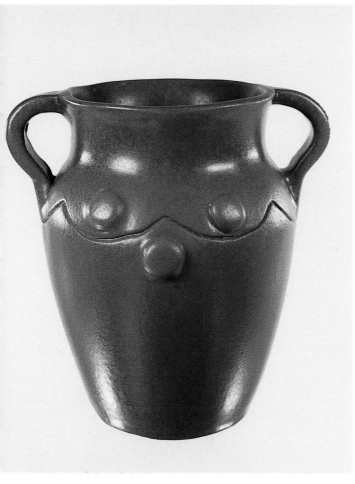

VASE 6 1/2"
Mk: Millie Lawson Oct 6, 1939 Welling Okla

STRAIGHT NECK VASE 6 1/2"
Mk: Winnie Simmer 1938-39 Sequoyah

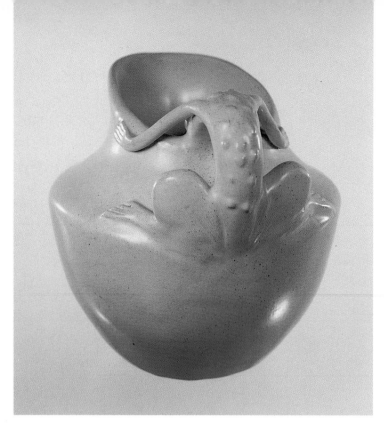

FROG HANDLE PITCHER 5"
Mk: Lula M. Thompson Sequoyah #18
Tan clay with off-white glaze.
All the Frog handles were applied by hand and look different. Three are shown.

FROG HANDLE PITCHER 5"
Mk: Levida Going 1938 Sequoyah

FROG HANDLE PITCHER 5"
Left Mk: Lena Welling Ok L. P.
Right: Another view of an earlier description.

Notice the different handle applications.

PLANTER 3 1/2"
Mk: E.M. Welling Okla

VASE 7 1/2"
Mk: Mitties Lawson Oct. 20 Welling Okla. Cherokee Co.

DUCK ASHTRAY L-8" No. 38
Mk: Evelyn Vann Sequoyah 1939

DOG VASE 8" No. 31
Mk: Mildred Woody Sequoyah 1939

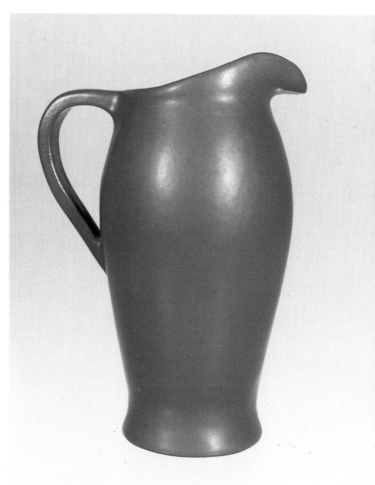

PITCHER 6"
Mk: Krouse Welling, Okla

VASE 5 1/2"
Mk: Mitties Lawson Oct 10, 1939 Welling, Okla
Glazed brown.

National Youth Administration Pottery (NYA) 1935-1943

After 1930, when a nation-wide depression swept over our country, Oklahoma—-like other states—-found itself unable to provide for all those in actual need through local agencies. The first help came in 1932 from the National Government in the form of many government relief administrations. This aid continued to come for about ten years.

In July of 1935, the Works Progress Administration (WPA) began taking over relief cases by providing work for able-bodied persons in need of help. The National Youth Administration (NYA) was a part of this agency. It provided job training for unemployed youth and part-time work for needy students. Pottery making was included under this program.

No specific information has been found in regard to which Oklahoma schools made NYA pottery. We believe it was made in public schools that taught art and, more specifically, those who taught ceramics and had trained teachers and proper equipment (kilns, etc.). Some Colleges and Universities should qualify, since they usually had ceramic departments in their art schools. The University of Oklahoma is a most likely candidate, since we know much ceramic art work was done there in the 1930s. Some larger and more advanced high schools may have made pottery, but it is unlikely.

The NYA was placed under the Federal Security Agency in 1939. In 1942 it was transferred to the Bureau of Training-War Manpower Commission. The NYA was terminated in 1943.

Mark found on NYA Pottery

BOTTLE VASES 5 1/2"
Notice the bottle interiors, the left one is black and the right is blue.

BOTTLE VASES 5 1/2"
Both have blue interiors.

BOTTLE PITCHER 5"

YELLOWARE PITCHER 20-OZ.

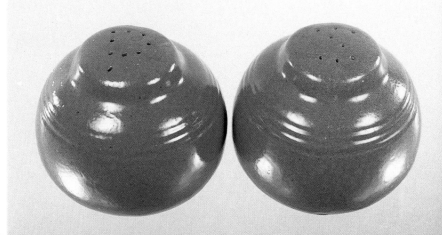

SALT & PEPPER SHAKERS 2 1/2"

Synar Ceramics
Muskogee, Oklahoma
1947-1959

Synar Ceramics was a dream come true for a lady artist named Elizabeth. As a little girl on a beautiful farm in Washington State where she was born, Elizabeth learned soap carving from her mother. She loved art and realized the creative spirit that was within her. Her mother always encouraged her and was a true friend. Her father, a very gentle and talented man, was seriously injured in an accident when she was a small child. Elizabeth Taylor was the name of this artist to be.

Elizabeth received her formal art education at the University of Washington in Seattle, and later at the University of San Diego in California, where she and her mother lived at the beginning of World War II. While living in California, Elizabeth met a Marine Corps pilot from Oklahoma by the name of Stanley Synar. They were married just before he went off to war. Elizabeth worked on the production line in an Aircraft Plant making B-24 Bombers until the war ended and her husband returned home.

The Synars came to Muskogee, Oklahoma in 1945. The next year they moved to her in-laws old home place in Warner. The house was not modern, but it was here that Elizabeth started "Synar Ceramics" in an emptied bedroom. She had but one small kiln and mixed her clay in the washing machine.

She soon moved the operation to a new small building along the highway. Pottery was made and sold there until the early 1950s when Synar Ceramics moved to a leased parachute building at the then abandoned Davis Field Airport in Muskogee. Elizabeth's business soon outgrew this building, and moved into a large hangar at the same site. Sales continued to grow rapidly.

In 1956, with a loan from the Small Business Administration and the proceeds acquired by cashing-in a life insurance policy her mother had on her, Elizabeth was able to build a large new plant with a sales room on the edge of Muskogee, along the busy U.S. Highway 69. At this plant she worked with over sixty production people. Sales efforts were extensive. Synar Ceramics was represented each year at trade shows in many major U.S. cities. Radio, television and catalog advertising was used. At their peak, Synar Ceramics had sales exceeding one million dollars per year. They were recognized nationally for their quality products. They sold to many florist and major department stores, such as Marshall-Field in Chicago and Neiman-Marcus in Dallas. Elizabeth, a pilot, flew herself to many shows and meetings. She also sold overseas to England.

Synar manufactured art pottery, with the exception of one dinnerware pattern made in the late '50s. Their main items were flower bowls and vases, figurines and specialty items such as ash trays. The dinnerware with serving pieces were made for a very short period of time. From the beginning of manufacturing in Warner, all pottery was marked either "Synar Ceramics" or "S.C."

Elizabeth did the art design work and prepared the clay and glazes. The clay came from Tennessee. The production people became highly skilled through both her training and her quest for perfection. It was a team effort with her leading.

In 1958, personal problems led to the closing of the business. It was purchased by John Frank of Frankoma Pottery of Sapulpa in September of 1958. The business continued to operate under the Synar name until, in 1959, John renamed it "GRACETONE POTTERY".

Elizabeth Synar Cramer still lives in Oklahoma and is very active in art. Her works in painting and sculpture are in great demand all over the country. She also enjoys writing poetry and does many large interior decorating projects. Her knowledge and creativity have resulted in lasting contributions to art and especially "Oklahoma Pottery".

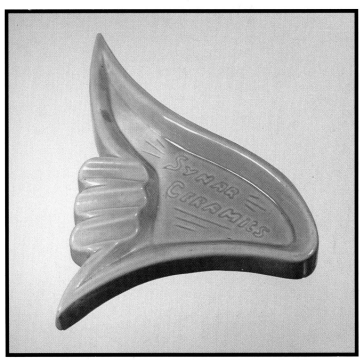

ADVERTISING "SYNAR CERAMICS" ASHTRAY 5"

CANNIBAL 4 1/2"

PINE CONE VASE 11"
Woodpine and Aqua

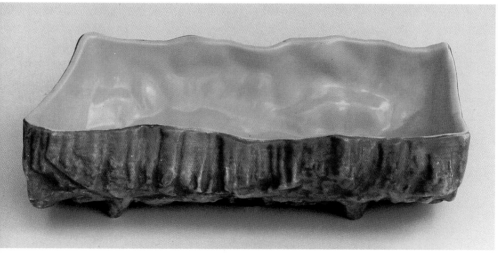

CORK BARK BOWL 11"
Woodpine and Aqua

WHEAT VASE 10"
Woodpine and Aqua

PLANTER W-6" Alligator glaze
ROUND PLANTER   5"
Wintergreen glaze
SQUARE FOOTED VASE
4 1/2"

HANDLED VASE   7 1/2"

BASKET   7 1/2"
Woodpine and Aqua

DEEP BOWL   13 1/2" x 5"
Woodpine and Aqua

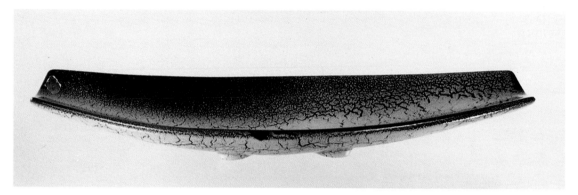

SHALLOW BOWL   16"
Wintergreen glaze

WALL POCKET   8"
Wintergreen glaze

SYNAR CHRISTMAS CARD 1959

John Frank continued the tradition he and Grace Lee had begun in 1944 of mailing ceramic Christmas cards to friends and their wholesale dealers.

This card is made with white Synar clay and marked: "SYNAR CHRIST-MAS 1959", indicating the company was still under the Synar name in December when the Christmas cards were produced. (This card was the one Frankoma gave away as their Christmas card in 1958.)

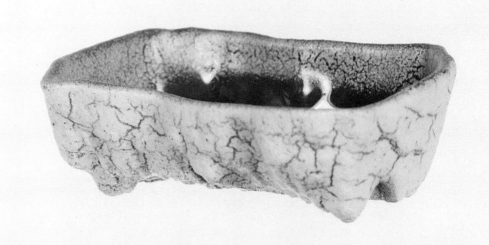

LOTUS BOWL 5 1/2"
Wintergreen glaze
OVAL PLANTER 4 1/2"
Black & White Straw glaze

BOWL 10" Straw glaze, inside Chartreuse
Very unusual bowl, lower side is 3" and higher side is 5". This would be an excellent bowl for popcorn.

Gracetone Pottery Muskogee, Oklahoma 1959-1967

In September of 1958 John Frank purchased a ceramic business named "SYNAR CERAMICS" (Muskogee, Oklahoma), located approximately fifty miles southeast of Tulsa.

Soon afterward Mr. J. C. Taylor, a Frankoma employee, moved to Muskogee to manage the new business under Mr. Frank's supervision. The business continued to be operated under the name of Synar until Mr. Frank renamed it–sometime in December of 1959–"GRACETONE POTTERY", after his wife Grace Lee.

Starting the new company presented many problems, financial and otherwise. To help defray expenses during the first year or so of operation, the plant made use of materials acquired in the purchase. These included sales brochures, molds and a white bodied clay.

Sometime after the change of name, the transition was made to the Frankoma's red firing clay and soon Gracetone Pottery had its own sales catalogs and some new molds and glazes (offering not only art ware and vases, but a beautiful line of dinnerware called "Orbit"). This pattern was made using a circular motif, some of the circles being pierced. It was available in three glaze colors: Pink Champagne, Cinnamon and Aqua.

Gracetone was competitive in price but the sales department prevented the growth and success of the company. Gracetone had only two sales representatives and their loyalties seemed to lie elsewhere.

Mr. Frank eventually considered Gracetone Pottery a losing proposition and gave the order to stop production on May 31, 1962. Mr. Taylor purchased the company and some of the equipment from Frankoma at that time. He moved into his own building in Muskogee and on June 1, 1963 resumed operations on a much smaller scale. Having no salesman, Mr. Taylor sold mainly to the retail trade and a few wholesale florist accounts. He made only a very limited amount of dinnerware.

Eventually he came to the same conclusion as John Frank and stopped production, closing the doors permanently on February 28, 1967.

Most all Gracetone Pottery is marked "GRACETONE". A few pieces have been found bearing only a gold foil sticker. One reads "POTTERY BY GRACETONE, MUSKOGEE, OKLA." and another merely says "SOUVENIR OF OKLAHOMA".

LARGE ENGLISH SETTER 5 1/2" Glaze-Cinnamon
LARGE TERRIER 5 1/2" Glaze-White, White Clay (Synar)

HOUND DOG 6" Glaze-Cinnamon
All three dogs (originally Frankoma's) were probably produced during the 1959-1962 period. All are rare!

TALL VASE 10 1/2" No. 120
Glaze-Rubbed Bisque, Jade
Green Inside.

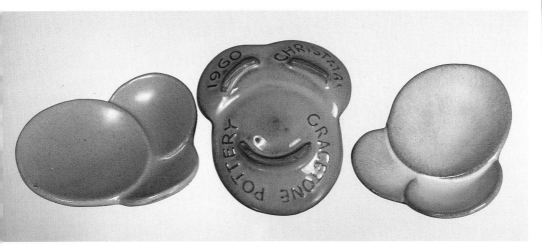

GRACETONE POTTERY CHRISTMAS CARDS 1960
Glaze-Pink Champagne, Aqua and Cinnamon
The Christmas Card has also been found in Gunmetal, a rich,
dull black glaze.

GLAD VASE 10 1/2" No. 119
BOTTLE VASE 9 1/2" No. 14
Glaze-Cinnamon

PEDESTALLED BOWL 6" No. 100P
Glaze-Gunmetal

127

"ORBIT" DINNERWARE
SUGAR W/LID & CREAMER
Glaze-Cinnamon
SALT & PEPPER Glaze-Pink
Champagne

CUP 7 OZ. & SAUCER   5"
DINNER PLATE   10"
SALAD PLATE   7"
FRUIT BOWL   6"
Glaze-Pink Champagne

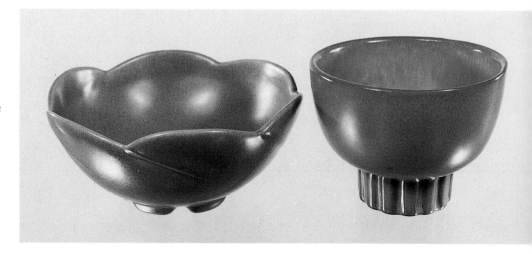

SCALLOPED BOWL   6"
No. 101   Glaze-Pink Champagne
ROUND PLANTER   4 1/2"
No. 304 Glaze-Cinnamon

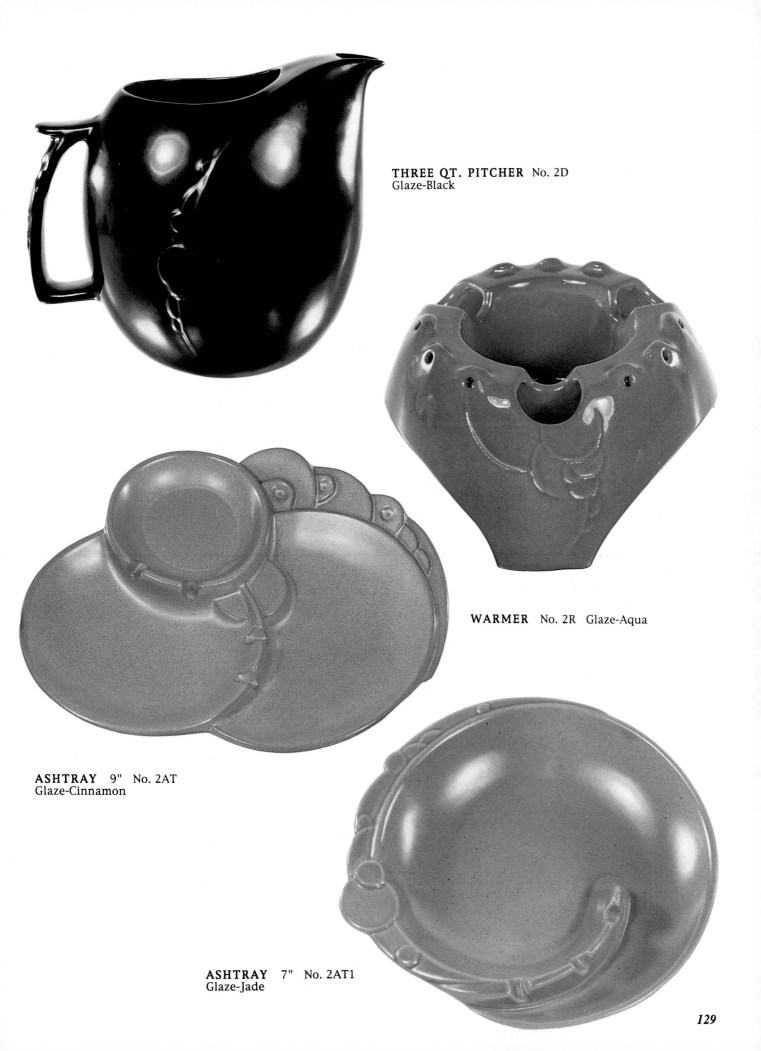

THREE QT. PITCHER No. 2D
Glaze-Black

WARMER No. 2R Glaze-Aqua

ASHTRAY 9" No. 2AT
Glaze-Cinnamon

ASHTRAY 7" No. 2AT1
Glaze-Jade

Creek Pottery
Checotah, Oklahoma
Circa 1970-1976

The Creek Indian Nation of Oklahoma became involved with "Creek Pottery" as a means of helping reduce unemployment among their people. The Bureau of Indian Affairs was instrumental in creating this new business.

Chief W. E. "Dode" McIntosh helped start the project in about 1969. He contacted his friend John Frank, of Frankoma Pottery, for help. In 1970, John Frank started training people to make pottery. He donated equipment, materials and personnel to help them. For his efforts, he was made an Honorary Creek Chief for life. After starting production, the plant worked about fifteen people.

A manufacturing plant was built at Checotah, close to U.S. Interstate Highway 40. Only art pottery was made. Most pottery was wholesaled to businesses in Oklahoma and surrounding states. It was also sold in the plant sales room and briefly at a retail outlet near Macon, Georgia. Only brochures were used for advertising. The business closed in early 1976.

Mark:

HORSE (ANIMATED) 4 1/2"

LARGE MALLARD   7 1/2" x 9"
SMALL MALLARD   5 1/2" x 7 1/2"

VASE 10"

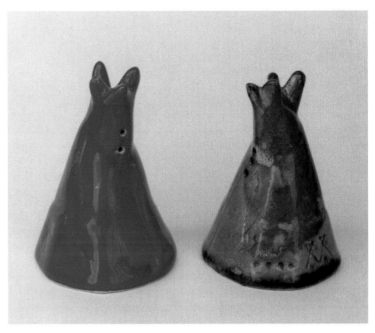

TEPEE SALT & PEPPER 3"
Originally Frankoma's mold. This is one of many Frankoma molds John Frank gave to the Creek Indian Nation to reproduce.

DUCK EGG CUP 3 1/2"

OWL FIGURINE/BOOK END 6"
INDIAN HEAD MUG/TOMA-
HAWK HANDLE 4 1/2"

PLANTER 4 1/2"

INDIAN HEAD/BUFFALO NICKEL BANK 7 1/2"
Pictured on the other side is an Indian head.

INDIAN MOCCASIN 8"
Attached is a gold sticker which
reads: "AUTHENTIC INDIAN
POTTERY MADE IN CHECOTAH, OK
- USA".

Cherokee Pottery
Porum, Oklahoma
1977-Present

"Cherokee Pottery" was started in Porum, Oklahoma by Howard Plunkett in 1977 and is still in business today. Mr. Plunkett is a member of the Cherokee Nation and a former employee of the Bureau of Indian Affairs. Today, hand painted Indian pottery is their main product. It is sold retail and wholesale. The pieces pictured are of their old product line and are no longer being made. Almost all Cherokee Pottery is dated. At peak production, over thirty people are employed. Howard Plunkett's personal art work is signed "Little Hawk", his Cherokee name.

Mark: 

QUAIL 6" Date: 11-10-81

INDIAN BOWL 12" No Date
Eight different animals are pictured around the bowl. A very nice piece.

INDIAN HEAD BUST 15"
Date: 6-1-83

HORSE 6" Date: 7-11-84

BUNNIES 4 3/4" Date: 2-1-88

BUFFALO 7 1/2" x 12"

DINNERWARE
PLATE	9 1/2"	Date: 3-26-80
BOWL	9"	Date: 10-14-83
BOWL	10 OZ.	Date: 5-23-81
CUP	7 OZ.	Date: 11-13-80

"HONEY" BEAR W/SPOON   6 1/2"   Date: 9-7-83
The tip of the spoon handle is the tongue.

RING HANDLED BOTTLE   12"   Date: 1-11-82

Other Oklahoma Artists

Oscar B. Jacobson came to the University of Oklahoma in the mid-twenties and was instrumental in developing the art department. He soon recognized the art talent of native American Indians and was able to get a student scholarship program started for them. Acee Blue Eagle, now deceased, is probably the most popular artist known who was a student at OU under this program.

ACEE BLUE EAGLE'S INDIAN PLAQUE
7 1/2"
Mk: Blue Eagle

ACEE BLUE EAGLE'S POLYNESIAN WOMAN 9"
Mk: Blue Eagle

OSCAR JACO BSON'S "GNOME"
(Fabled dwarf) 8"
Mk: Jacobson
Jacobson was of Scandinavian descent.

R. W. HILSMEYER'S VASE 5"
Dated 6-22-32
Mk: Hilsmeyer

IDRESS ASH'S PLATE   10" Diam.
Mk: Idress Ash

BELVA CLEMENT'S BOWL 7" Diam.
Dated 1933
Mk: Clement

GEORGE FORSYTH'S VASE
7 1/2"
Dated 1941
Mk: G. Forsyth

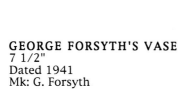

A Final Word From The Authors

We who are living upon the earth today are seeing a new day. The government has failed us. There's no security in the economy any more. Oh, there will be a brief recovery, but it will be short-lived. Even the weather across the United States seems to be warning us "there's something about to happen."

The Lord has given us a message to share with you..."This world is on the eve of destruction. But before destruction comes I am sending a revival, a sweeping wave of My Spirit to gather men and women unto Me. If men had believed there was a flood coming, they would have helped Noah build the ark. They were too busy, eating, drinking, marrying and giving in marriage until the day of the flood came. Destruction is coming! But first will come a flood of My Spirit in grace and then will come a flood of judgment upon those who have rejected Me. The hour is at hand, now is the time to work. Do not allow the cares of this world to pull you away from doing My will."

The bible says in Deuteronomy 30:19..."I call Heaven and earth to witness this day against you, that I have set before you life and death, the blessing and the curse; therefore choose life, that you and your descendants may live."

Which will you choose?

God loves you and is not holding your sins against you. Jesus paid the price for our sins, so that through Him, we can have life, eternal life! (John 3:35-36, John 3:15) Only through Jesus can we obtain eternal life.

Romans 10:9-10 says: "If you confess with your mouth that Jesus is Lord and believe in your heart that God has raised Him from the dead, you shall be saved. For with the heart man believes unto righteousness; and with the mouth confession is made unto salvation." Verse 13 goes on to say: "Whoever calls upon the name of the Lord (Jesus) shall be saved."

Jesus said, "Him who comes to Me I will most certainly not cast out - I will never, no never reject one of them who come to Me." John 6:37 No matter what you have done, you can go to Jesus and He will accept you.

Ask Him into your heart today.

Phyllis and Tom Bess
14535 East 13th Street
Tulsa, Oklahoma 74108
Telephone: (918) 437-7776

Bibliography

A Guide to the Indian Tribes of Oklahoma, Muriel H. Wright, University of Oklahoma Press, 1951.

American Indian Painters, J.O Snodgrass, New York Museum of The American Indian, 1968.

Cherokee Advocate Newspaper, Tahlequah, Oklahoma, July 1993.

Frankoma Pottery Catalogs, 1936 to 1994.

Frankoma Treasures, self-published, Phyllis & Tom Bess, 1983.

Oklahoma, The Story of A State, E.E. Dale, Row, Peterson and Co., 1950.

Price Guide

Prices vary immensely according to the condition of the piece, the location of the market, and the overall quality of the design and manufacture. Condition is always of paramount importance in assigning a value. Price in the Midwest differ from those in the West or East, and those at specialty antique shows will vary from those at general shows. And, of course, being at the right palce at the right time can make all the difference.

All these factors make it impossible to create an absolutely accurate price list, but we can offer a guide. The prices reflect what one could realistically expect to pay at retail or aution. The number in the left hand column is the page number. The center column provides a brief description of the item. The right hand column contains the estimated price ranges in United States dollars.

Tamac high-range prices should apply to pieces glazed in Butterscotch, Raspberry and Honey, since these are the most scarce colors.

Page	Description	Price
3	HAMMAT CHRISTMAS TREE TRAY	$40.00-50.00
4	*FRANKOMA MOTHER BIRD	7.00
	*FRANKOMA BABY BIRD	7.00

FRANKOMA POTTERY

Page	Description	Price
6	BUFFALO	400.00-500.00
9	MINIATURE TEAPOT	30.00-35.00
	BUD VASE	35.00-45.00
	MINIATURE PUMA	35.00-45.00
	MINIATURE AZTEC PITCHER	10.00-15.00
	CATTLEBRAND TRIVET	10.00-15.00
	MINIATURE TEPEE VASE	5.00-8.00
	MINIATURE DONKEY	85.00-100.00
	MINIATURE RINGED VASE	25.00-30.00
	MINIATURE WALKING ELEPHANT	85.00-100.00
10	DOGWOOD CANDLEHOLDER	10.00-15.00
	LAMP OF KNOWLEDGE CANDLEHOLDER	35.00-45.00
	PETER PAN MASK	50.00-75.00
	STEIN	20.00-25.00
	WAR GOD MUG	20.00-25.00
	BUD VASE	15.00-20.00
	*FREE FORM VASE/ CANDLEHOLDER	8.00
	FANDANCER, Woodland Moss	325.00-375.00
11	CORNUCOPIA	10.00-20.00
	HEXAGONAL VASE	10.00-15.00
	SINGLE CANDLEHOLDER	10.00-15.00
	PEDESTALLED BOWL	35.00-45.00
	*SEATED PUMA	15.00
	Ada Clay	75.00-100.00
	W/Pacing Leopard Logo	250.00-300.00
	*BOOT MUG	9.00
12	VASE	150.00-200.00
	Marked "FRANK POTTERIES"	500.00-600.00
	PINACLE VASE, Marked "FRANK POTTERIES"	300.00-400.00
	VASE 4"	75.00-85.00
	W/Pacing Leopard Logo	125.00-175.00
	Marked "FRANK POTTERIES"	250.00-300.00
	VASE 6 1/2"	
	W/Pacing Leopard Logo	150.00-200.00
	Marked "FRANK POTTERIES"	250.00-300.00
	FLOWER BOWL, Marked "FRANK POTTERIES"	225.00-275.00
	VASE 3 3/4"	75.00-90.00
	W/Pacing Leopard Logo	125.00-175.00
	Marked "FRANK POTTERIES"	225.00-275.00
	VASE 2 5/8"	25.00-35.00
	W/Pacing Leopard Logo	125.00-150.00
	Marked "FRANK POTTERIES"	175.00-200.00
	LARGE INDIAN JAR	150.00-200.00
	W/Pacing Leopard Logo	250.00-300.00
	Marked "FRANK POTTERIES"	400.00-500.00
13	PACING LEOPARD SIGN	600.00-700.00
	TEPEE SIGN	350.00-450.00
	THIRD FRANKOMA SIGN	75.00-90.00
	*FOURTH FRANKOMA SIGN	15.00
14	FISH FLOWER FROG	500.00-600.00
	COATI-MUNDI	800.00-1,000.00
	WALKING OCELOT	300.00-400.00
	CHARGING TIGER	450.00-550.00
	DEER GROUP	650.00-750.00
15	SWAN FLOWER FROG	300.00-350.00
	PEKINGESE DOG	375.00-475.00
	W/Pacing Leopard Logo	475.00-550.00
	Marked "TAYLOR"	550.00-650.00
	MERMAID FLOWER FROG	1,000.00-1,200.00
	HOUND DOG	450.00-550.00
16	COYOTE PUP	400.00-500.00
	Marked "TAYLOR"	500.00-600.00
	PRANCING PERCHERON	300.00-400.00
	REARING CLYDESDALE	150.00-200.00
	Ada Clay	250.00-300.00
	CIRCUS HORSE	75.00-95.00
	Ada Clay	95.00-125.00
	Glaze not available after 1942	150.00-200.00
	PRANCING COLT	550.00-650.00
17	CAMEL	425.00-475.00
	COWBOY	400.00-425.00
	W/"RODEO, WOODWARD, OK"	425.00-450.00
	BUFFALO	400.00-500.00
18	**INDIAN BOWL MAKER	45.00-60.00
	Ada Clay	95.00-125.00
	W/Pacing Leopard Logo	175.00-200.00
	Marked "TAYLOR"	450.00-550.00
	TOAS SQUAW	1,000.00-1,200.00
	FANDANCER	150.00-200.00
	Ada Clay	300.00-400.00
19	**INDIAN CHIEF	45.00-60.00
	Ada Clay	85.00-125.00
	W/Hand Painted Headdress	250.00-300.00
	TORCH SINGER	1,000.00-1,200.00
	HARLAM HOOFER	1,000.00-1,200.00
	FANDANCER W/Matching DEEP PLATTER	350.00-450.00
20	TORCH SINGER	1,000.00-1,200.00
	HARLAM HOOFER	1,000.00-1,200.00
	MADONNA	175.00-225.00
	AMAZON WOMAN	400.00-500.00
	ENGLISH SETTER MINIATURE VASE	75.00-85.00
	ENGLISH SETTER MINIATURE	60.00-65.00
	LARGE ENGLISH SETTER	175.00-225.00
21	GARDENER GIRL	80.00-85.00
	Prairie Green	90.00-100.00
	GARDENER BOY, Belted Pants & Shirt	90.00-100.00
	Prairie Green	100.00-110.00
	FLOWER GIRL	70.00-80.00
	GARDENER BOY, Bibbed Overalls	90.00-100.00
	Prairie Green	100.00-110.00
	BULL	45.00-50.00
	TROJAN HORSE	45.00-50.00
	SWAN	40.00-50.00
	DONKEY	90.00-100.00
	TERRIER	90.00-100.00
	PUMA	40.00-50.00
	ELEPHANT	45.00-50.00
	ENGLISH SETTER	60.00-65.00
22	TWO GIRLS	200.00-250.00
	WILLARD STONE	
	*INDIAN MAIDEN	13.50
	*COYOTE	13.50
	*SQUIRREL	9.00
	*INDIAN MADONNA	20.00
	*MARE & COLT	13.50
	*PONY TAIL GIRL	35.00
	MEDICINE MAN	125.00-150.00
	Ada Clay	185.00-225.00
23	PRANCING COLT BOOK END	250.00-300.00
	SEATED FIGURE BOOK END	225.00-250.00
	W/Pacing Leopard Logo	300.00-350.00
	Marked "TAYLOR"	450.00-550.00
	MOUNTAIN GIRL BOOK END	95.00-120.00
	Ada Clay	185.00-200.00
	WALKING OCELOT BOOK END, Each	185.00-225.00
	Marked "TAYLOR"	350.00-450.00
24	LEOPARD BOOK END	185.00-200.00
	W/Pacing Leopard Logo	350.00-450.00
	DREAMER GIRL BOOK END	180.00-225.00
	SEAHORSE BOOK END, Each	300.00-350.00
	BUCKING BRONCO BOOK END	125.00-175.00
	CHARGER HORSE BOOK END	70.00-85.00
	Ada Clay	125.00-165.00
25	*BOOT BOOK END, Pair	35.00
	RED IRISH SETTER BOOK END, Early	125.00-150.00
	RED IRISH SETTER BOOK END, Restyled	65.00-85.00
	Ada Clay	95.00-125.00
	COLLIE HEAD, Short Hair	70.00-80.00
	COLLIE HEAD, Long Hair	75.00-85.00
	Ada Clay	125.00-150.00
26	SMALL NEGRO MASK	100.00-125.00
	MINIATURE INDIAN MASK	15.00-20.00
	Ada Clay	25.00-35.00
	HAPPY INDIAN MASK	350.00-450.00
	INDIAN HEAD WALL POCKET W/Full Headdress	175.00-200.00
27	NEGRO HEAD WALL POCKET	125.00-150.00
	INDIAN HEAD WALL POCKET	125.00-150.00
	WALL POCKET W/Waterer	25.00-35.00
	BIRD HANDLE WALL POCKET	70.00-75.00
28	PHOEBE WALL POCKET, One Glaze	75.00-100.00
	Bisque W/Hand Painted Features	150.00-175.00
	BILLIKEN WALL POCKET	75.00-85.00
	RAM'S HEAD WALL POCKET	75.00-90.00
29	LEAF WALL POCKET, 12"	65.00-75.00
	LEAF WALL POCKET, 8 1/2"	40.00-50.00
	WAGON WHEEL WALL POCKET	35.00-40.00
	BOOT WALL POCKET 5"	55.00-65.00
	DUTCH SHOE WALL POCKET	35.00-40.00
	DUTCH SHOE PLANTER	15.00-25.00
30	CANDLEHOLDER, Pair	25.00-35.00
	Ada Clay	45.00-55.00
	SPIRAL CANDLEHOLDER, Pair	75.00-100.00
	W/Pacing Leopard Logo	150.00-175.00

Item	Price
CANDELABRUM	65.00-75.00
MONKS, Each	175.00-225.00
DOUBLE CANDLEHOLDER, Pair	15.00-25.00
Ada Clay	35.00-45.00
31 SHELL CANDLEHOLDER	25.00-30.00
DOUBLE CACTUS CANDLE-HOLDER	40.00-50.00
PEDESTALLED CANDLEHOLDER	15.00-20.00
DOGWOOD CANDLEHOLDER	10.00-15.00
WAGON WHEEL CANDLE-HOLDER	20.00-25.00
WAGON WHEEL ASHTRAY/CANDLEHOLDER	30.00-35.00
Ada Clay	35.00-45.00
SINGLE CANDLEHOLDER, Pair	25.00-35.00
"ROCKS" CANDLEHOLDER, Pair	45.00-50.00
PILLAR CANDLEHOLDER	15.00-20.00
32 HUMIDOR	200.00-250.00
ASHTRAY	15.00-20.00
BOOK ASHTRAY	25.00-30.00
DUTCH SHOE ASHTRAY 6", Pair	45.00-55.00
DUTCH SHOE ASHTRAY 4", Pair	25.00-35.00
33 ELEPHANT ASHTRAY	100.00-125.00
WALKING ELEPHANT	90.00-100.00
ARROWHEAD ASHTRAY	10.00-15.00
FREE FORM ASHTRAY	35.00-40.00
W/Later Handle	20.00-30.00
34 LEAF HANDLED VASE	350.00-400.00
GRECIAN VASE	300.00-350.00
ROUND JAR	200.00-250.00
35 TALL FLAT VASE	300.00-350.00
FIRESIDE VASE	350.00-400.00
TALL RAM'S HEAD VASE	100.00-150.00
SMALL RAM'S HEAD VASE	25.00-35.00
CHINESE BOTTLE VASE	50.00-65.00
Chinese Red Glaze	200.00-225.00
36 FISH FLOWER HOLDER	150.00-175.00
HOBBY HORSE FLOWER HOLDER	150.00-175.00
ELEPHANT FLOWER HOLDER	150.00-175.00
DUCK FLOWER HOLDER	150.00-175.00
IVY BOWL	85.00-95.00
Restyled Ivy Bowl	35.00-45.00
LEAF HANDLED VASE	45.00-65.00
Ada Clay	75.00-100.00
CENTERPIECE BOWL	25.00-35.00
Ada Clay	45.00-60.00
37 OVAL LOW BOWL 7"	15.00-20.00
W/Miniature Animal	55.00-65.00
W/Miniature Boot	25.00-35.00
SMALL ROUND JAR	45.00-55.00
ROUND JAR	35.00-45.00
MINT BOWL	15.00-25.00
Ada Clay	35.00-45.00
SMALL MINT BOWL	50.00-60.00
W/Pacing Leopard Logo	100.00-125.00
GRECIAN VASE, Terra Cotta, Glazed Handles	125.00-150.00
GRECIAN VASE, One Glaze	50.00-65.00
FLAT VASE	75.00-85.00
W/Pacing Leopard Logo	125.00-150.00
SMALL FLAT VASE	65.00-75.00
TALL CORNUCOPIA	15.00-25.00
Ada Clay	35.00-45.00
SMALL CORNUCOPIA	50.00-60.00
38 SMALL REED PILLOW VASE	35.00-40.00
LARGE REED PILLOW VASE	30.00-35.00
W/Flying Goose on Backside	20.00-25.00
FLOWERABRUM	75.00-100.00
BLACK FOOTED VASE	15.00-20.00
Ada Clay	25.00-35.00
Pierced	45.00-55.00
OBLONG FLOWER BOWL	25.00-35.00
39 LOW RECTANGULAR BOWL	10.00-15.00
PILLOW VASE	10.00-15.00
Ada Clay	15.00-25.00
ORIENTAL PILLOW VASE	30.00-40.00
FAN SHELL VASE	15.00-20.00
Ada Clay	30.00-40.00
SQUARE BOWL	25.00-30.00
ROUND BOWL	25.00-30.00
CARVED JAR	40.00-45.00
40 VASE/HONEY BOTTLE	25.00-35.00
Ada Clay	45.00-55.00
CHAMBERED NAUTILUS VASE	35.00-45.00
*CORNUCOPIA BOWL	20.00
Ada Clay	45.00-65.00
CORNUCOPIA	30.00-35.00
Ada Clay	45.00-60.00
MINI RINGED VASE	25.00-35.00
BUD VASE	45.00-55.00
BUD VASE	35.00-45.00
SMALL BULBOUS VASE	50.00-65.00
41 THUNDERBIRD PITCHER	80.00-90.00
THUNDERBIRD CANTEEN	20.00-30.00

Item	Price
Ada Clay	40.00-50.00
MINI THUNDERBIRD VASE	25.00-35.00
LARGE THUNDERBIRD VASE	80.00-90.00
MINI SNAIL PITCHER	10.00-15.00
MINI PITCHER	10.00-15.00
MINIATURE BOOT W/Star	15.00-25.00
Without Star	8.00-12.00
VASE	35.00-45.00
W/Pacing Leopard Logo	125.00-150.00
Marked "FRANK POTTERIES"	185.00-225.00
MINIATURE VASE	10.00-15.00
MINIATURE VASE	20.00-25.00
FIRESIDE VASE	65.00-75.00
Ada Clay	75.00-100.00
FIRESIDE PITCHER	65.00-75.00
Ada Clay	75.00-100.00
*SCALLOPED BOWL	16.00
Ada Clay	35.00-45.00
DEEP FREE FORM BOWL	25.00-35.00
Restyled Foot	15.00-25.00
42 BUD VASE	10.00-20.00
SNAIL BUD VASE	10.00-15.00
Ada Clay	25.00-35.00
TWO HANDLED BUD VASE	15.00-20.00
CROCUS BUD VASE	15.00-20.00
Ada Clay	25.00-35.00
CORK BARK BOWL	20.00-25.00
CORK BARK PLANTER	10.00-20.00
CORK BARK BOWL	15.00-20.00
ROUND DEEP CACTUS BOWL	15.00-20.00
CORK BARK ROUND BOWL	35.00-45.00
OBLONG BOWL	30.00-40.00
43 WAGON WHEEL VASE	15.00-20.00
Ada Clay	30.00-40.00
FREE FORM BUD VASE	10.00-15.00
FOOTED ROUND VASE	10.00-15.00
CORNUCOPIA	10.00-20.00
SHELL BOWL	25.00-35.00
TALL URN	20.00-30.00
THREE LEVEL VASE	25.00-35.00
PLANTER	15.00-20.00
POD VASE	15.00-20.00
44 CRESCENT BOWL	30.00-40.00
*OLD FASHION PITCHER SET	18.00
*Smaller Set	12.00
ALADDIN LAMP CANDLE-HOLDER	35.00-45.00
45 FREE FORM BOWL	20.00-30.00
FAN VASE	35.00-45.00
*SMALL SWAN PLANTER	12.00
Ada Clay	25.00-35.00
BASKET PLANTER	10.00-20.00
TURTLE PLANTER	20.00-30.00
46 POSTCARDS, Each	10.00-15.00
47 "CLAY IN THE MASTER'S HANDS" 1977	65.00-100.00
TOOTHBRUSH HOLDER	10.00-15.00
DOG BANK	65.00-75.00
COLLIE HEAD BANK	75.00-85.00
BANK W/Advertising	25.00-35.00
MALLARD BANK	35.00-45.00
48 JEWELRY, Ear Clips/Screws, Pair	20.00-25.00
On Original Card	30.00-35.00
Cuff Links, Pair	25.00-30.00
Dress Pin	15.00-20.00
OKLAHOMA'S SEMI-CENTENNIAL Pin	30.00-35.00
Lady's Bo	20.00-25.00
Bolo Ties	30.00-35.00
CACTI-PIN	45.00-55.00
*TURTLE PAPERWEIGHT	5.00
49 BONNET WOMAN MEDALLION	100.00-125.00
TEXAS COWBOY MEDALLION	100.00-125.00
WOMAN MEDALLION	85.00-100.00
50TH ANNIVERSARY BELL	20.00-25.00
MINIATURE CUP	30.00-35.00
WEDDING BELLS	50.00-65.00
"IOWA SUNSHINE" JUG	40.00-45.00
"TEXAS CENTENNIAL" JUG	75.00-100.00
50 OKLAHOMA EASTERN STAR PLATE	10.00-15.00
Acorn Wall Pocket	25.00-30.00
Individual Sugar	10.00-15.00
"UNCLE SLUG" JUG	15.00-20.00
"POE'S LIQUORS"	20.00-25.00
"TULSARAMA!" ASHTRAY	25.00-35.00
LAMP OF KNOWLEDGE CANDLEHOLDER	35.00-45.00
LAMP OF KNOWLEDGE TRAY	30.00-40.00
51 "ANN'S BAKERY" DONUT ASHTRAY	25.00-35.00
"ROMAN NOSE" ASHTRAY	35.00-45.00
"JOHN FRANK" APPRECIATION BOWLS, Each	35.00-45.00
"FRANKOMA POTTERY AWARD" VASE	75.00-100.00

Item	Price
"TERPSICHORE" WALL PLAQUE	25.00-35.00
52 LORD'S SUPPER CHALICE	25.00-35.00
PRESBYTERIAN TOKEN	20.00-25.00
OIL DERRICK SALT & PEPPER	20.00-25.00
TURNER TURNPIKE SALT & PEPPER	25.00-30.00
HORSESHOE SALT & PEPPER	20.00-25.00
"BILL WHITE CHEVROLET" ASHTRAY	20.00-25.00
53 ORCHID MUG	15.00-20.00
FRANKOMA'S 50TH ANNIVERSARY MUG	35.00-45.00
BLOSSOM SHOP MUG	15.00-20.00
THE BRAILLE PLATE, Rubbed Bisque	100.00-125.00
White Sand	65.00-75.00
CONESTOGA WAGON PLATE	85.00-125.00
FRANKOMA'S 50TH ANNIVERSARY TRAY	30.00-35.00
54 ORNAMENT	20.00-25.00
POTTERY SHOW SIGN	35.00-50.00
"OKLAHOMA LAND RUN" PLATE	15.00-25.00
*TEXAS STATE PLATE	9.50
*SOONER STATE PLATE	9.50
*"FRANKOMA, 60TH ANNIVERSARY" PLATE	25.00
55 COOKIE JAR, Knob Handle	75.00-100.00
Animal Handle	200.00-225.00
W/Silver Overlay	250.00-275.00
CANISTER SET, MAYAN-AZTEC	100.00-125.00
*CANISTER SET, RINGED	84.00
CANISTER SET, SCALLOPED BASE, OPEN HANDLES	150.00-200.00
Restyled Handles	100.00-125.00
GUERNSEY PITCHER	35.00-45.00
Oldest Mark	65.00-85.00
GUERNSEY MINIATURE PITCHER	10.00-15.00
GUERNSEY CREAMER	30.00-35.00
W/Advertising	45.00-50.00
LARGE GUERNSEY PITCHER W/Lid	100.00-125.00
W/Pacing Leopard Logo	175.00-200.00
56 *WARMER 8"	11.00
*WARMER 6"	9.00
CONDIMENT JUGS, Each	35.00-50.00
TABLE BELL, Each	10.00-15.00
NAPKIN HOLDER	15.00-20.00
57 ELEPHANT SALT & PEPPER	65.00-75.00
BULL SALT & PEPPER	55.00-65.00
PUMA SALT & PEPPER	55.00-65.00
WAGON WHEEL SHAKER	5.00-10.00
*WESTWIND SHAKER	6.00
*MAYAN AZTEC SHAKER, SMALL	6.00
MAYAN AZTEC SHAKER, LARGE	10.00-20.00
*PLAINSMAN SHAKER, SMALL	6.00
PLAINSMAN SHAKER, LARGE	10.00-15.00
LAZYBONES SALT & PEPPER	10.00-15.00
BARRELL SALT & PEPPER	15.00-20.00
GUERNSEY SALT & PEPPER	30.00-40.00
SNAIL SHAKER	10.00-15.00
*MILK CAN SALT & PEPPER	15.00
WHEAT SHOCK SALT & PEPPER	10.00-15.00
Ada Clay	18.00-20.00
SUGAR & CREAMER	75.00-100.00
58 SUGAR & CREAMER	50.00-75.00
*WESTWIND 2-CUP TEAPOT	12.00
WAGON WHEELS 2-CUP TEAPOT	20.00-30.00
MAYAN AZTEC 2-CUP TEAPOT	35.00-45.00
*MAYAN AZTEC 2-CUP TEAPOT, Restyled	12.00
SUGAR W/LID	50.00-60.00
CRACKER TRAY	150.00-200.00
59 MAYAN AZTEC INDIVIDUAL BAKER	35.00-45.00
BARREL INDIVIDUAL BAKER	35.00-45.00
WAGON WHEELS INDIVIDUAL BAKER	35.00-45.00
LAZYBONES INDIVIDUAL BAKER	30.00-40.00
PLAINSMAN INDIVIDUAL BAKER	30.00-40.00
TEAPOT 8-CUP	75.00-100.00
TEACUP	25.00-30.00
LARGE TEA PITCHER	125.00-150.00
Two Glazes	150.00-175.00
TEACUP, Each	30.00-35.00
Two Glazes	35.00-45.00
60 ICED TEA PITCHER	45.00-55.00
BATTER PITCHER	30.00-35.00
BARREL PITCHER	25.00-35.00
BARREL MUG	15.00-20.00
*MAYAN AZTEC PITCHER	20.00

	Ada Clay	45.00-50.00
	W/Pacing Leopard Logo	125.00-150.00
	*MAYAN AZTEC STEINS, Each	10.00
	Ada Clay	20.00-30.00
	W/Pacing Leopard Logo	45.00-55.00
61	*ONE-HALF GALLON PITCHER	24.00
	Ada Clay	40.00-45.00
	W/Pacing Leopard Logo	95.00-125.00
	MUG, W/Pacing Leopard Logo, Each	65.00-75.00
	JUICE JUG W/STOPPER	45.00-50.00
	REFRIGERATOR JUG W/ STOPPER	55.00-70.00
	BABY MUG, Each	25.00-30.00
62	CHILD'S "MOUSE" PLATE & MUG	15.00-20.00
	LAZYBONES 10" PLATE	10.00-12.00
	LAZYBONES CUP & SAUCER	10.00-15.00
	LAZYBONES SUGAR W/LID	10.00-15.00
	WAGONWHEEL TRIVET	45.00-55.00
	LAZYBONES TRIVET	45.00-55.00
63	WAGON WHEELS TEAPOT 6-CUP	25.00-35.00
	Ada Clay	40.00-50.00
	WAGON WHEELS TEAPOT 2-CUP	15.00-25.00
	Ada Clay	24.00-35.00
	WAGON WHEEL CREAMER	10.00-14.00
	WAGON WHEEL SALT & PEPPER	10.00-15.00
	WAGON WHEEL SUGAR	10.00-14.00
	WAGON WHEEL CUP & SAUCER	8.00-12.00
	Ada Clay	14.00-18.00
	WAGON WHEEL PLATE	10.00-12.00
	Ada Clay	14.00-18.00
	WAGON WHEEL DESSERT	4.00-5.00
	Ada Clay	6.00-8.00
64	WAGON WHEEL 1 QT. VEG BOWL	10.00-15.00
	Ada Clay	15.00-20.00
	WAGON WHEEL DEEP PLATTER	15.00-20.00
	Ada Clay	20.00-30.00
65	CHRISTMAS CARDS Any little pitcher or tray without the Christmas message would be valued from $10.00 - $20.00 each.	
	1944	95.00-105.00
	1947-48	75.00-85.00
	1949	55.00-65.00
	1950-51	65.00-75.00
	1952	75.00-85.00
	1953-54	65.00-75.00
66	1955-56	65.00-75.00
	1957-58	60.00-70.00
	1959-60	55.00-65.00
	1961-63	50.00-60.00
	1964-66	50.00-60.00
	1967-68	40.00-50.00
	1969-71	30.00-40.00
	1972	30.00-35.00
	1973-74	25.00-30.00
	1975-79	25.00-30.00
	1980-82	20.00-25.00
67	1975	100.00-110.00
	1976-77	75.00-85.00
	1978-79	70.00-80.00
	1980-82	60.00-70.00
	1984-88	50.00-60.00
	1989 (Last Year)	50.00-60.00
68	CHRISTMAS PLATES	
	1965	300.00-335.00
	1966	75.00-90.00
	1967	70.00-80.00
	1968	50.00-60.00
	1969-70	35.00-45.00
	1971-75	30.00-40.00
	1976-80	25.00-35.00
	1981-90	24.00-30.00
	1991-93	20.00-25.00
	1994	19.00

POLITICAL MUGS

69	ELEPHANT MUG	
	1974 "NIXON-FORD"	200.00-250.00
	1968	75.00-95.00
	1969	65.00-85.00
	1970-71	55.00-65.00
	1972	40.00-50.00
	1973	45.00-55.00
	1974	35.00-45.00
	ELEPHANT OR DONKEY MUG	
	1975-76	30.00-40.00
	1977-79	25.00-35.00
	1980-85	20.00-30.00
	1986-90	20.00-30.00
	1991-93	15.00-20.00
	1994	10.00

69	LIMITED EDITION VASES	
	V-1	85.00-100.00
	V-2	65.00-80.00
	V-3	75.00-85.00
	V-4	80.00-90.00
	V-5	80.00-90.00
	V-6	80.00-90.00
	V-7	75.00-85.00
	V-8	70.00-80.00
	V-9	70.00-80.00
	V-10	40.00-50.00
	V-11	40.00-50.00
	V-12	45.00-55.00
	V-13	45.00-55.00
	V-14	75.00-85.00
	V-15	55.00-65.00
70	WILDLIFE PLATES	
	1972-75	65.00-100.00
	1977-79	55.00-85.00
	TEENAGERS OF THE BIBLE	
	1972	35.00-45.00
	1974-75	35.00-45.00
	1976	40.00-50.00
	1977-82	25.00-35.00
71	BICENTENNIAL PLATES, Each	35.00-45.00
	TOBY MUGS, Each	15.00-20.00
	Without Date	10.00-15.00
72	MADONNA PLATES	
	1977-78	25.00-30.00
	*1981 & 1986	20.00

TAMAC POTTERY

74	OKLAHOMA ASHTRAY	10.00-15.00
	W/Advertising	15.00-20.00
	ASHTRAYS, Each	10.00-15.00
75	LARGE VIOLET PLANTER	10.00-15.00
	BIRD	15.00-20.00
	SMALL VIOLET PLANTER	10.00-15.00
	BUD VASE	10.00-15.00
	DISH GARDEN	15.00-20.00
	LARGE MANTEL PLANTER	25.00-30.00
	FREE FORM VASE	20.00-25.00
76	WALL VASE, Each	10.00-15.00
	SINGLE CANDLEHOLDER	10.00-15.00
	DOUBLE CANDLEHOLDER	15.00-20.00
	SALT & PEPPER	8.00-10.00
	SUGAR W/LID	10.00-12.00
	CREAMER	6.00-8.00
	SUGAR & CREAMER, INDIVIDUAL SET	20.00-25.00
77	DECANTER	55.00-60.00
	TEAPOT/CHOCOLATE POT	70.00-75.00
	TEAPOT W/LID 6-CUP	70.00-75.00
78	PITCHER 4 QT.	25.00-30.00
	PITCHER 2 QT.	30.00-35.00
	PITCHER, JUICE	25.00-30.00
	DECANTER GOBLET	10.00-15.00
	TUMBLER	8.00-12.00
	JUICE TUMBLER	8.00-10.00
	BARBECUE PLATE	12.00-15.00
	BARBECUE CUP	6.00-8.00
79	BARBECUE PLATE	12.00-15.00
	DINNER PLATE	8.00-10.00
	SALAD PLATE	8.00-9.00
	BARBECUE CUP	6.00-8.00
	BARBECUE SAUCER	5.00-7.00
80	COFFEE CUP	6.00-8.00
	TEACUP	5.00-10.00
	SAUCER	3.00-4.00
	MUG	12.00-15.00
	DEMITASSE CUP	12.00-15.00
	DEMITASSE SAUCER	8.00-10.00
	BUTTER DISH	25.00-35.00
	GRAVYBOAT	15.00-20.00
	COVERED CASSEROLE 2 QT.	45.00-50.00
	UNDERPLATE/PLATTER 12"	15.00-20.00
	UNDERPLATE/PLATTER 18"	25.00-30.00
81	SERVING BOWL 1 QT.	8.00-10.00
	SERVING BOWL 2 QT.	12.00-15.00
	FRUIT BOWL	6.00-8.00
	DIVIDED RELISH DISH	15.00-20.00
	SPOON REST	10.00-15.00
82	ASHTRAY W/ADVERTISING	15.00-20.00
	SPOON REST W/ADVERTISING	15.00-20.00
	PLATE W/ADVERTISING	15.00-20.00
	POSTCARD	10.00-15.00

HAMMAT ORIGINALS

84	MONKEY	65.00-75.00
	FRUIT CENTER PIECE	50.00-55.00
	CANDLEHOLDERS, Pair	30.00-35.00
85	CLOWN HEAD	40.00-50.00
	MONKEY	35.00-45.00
	"AKDAR" FIGURINE	15.00-20.00

	INDIAN MAIDEN WALL MASK	15.00-20.00
	RAM	75.00-85.00
86	MASK MUGS, Each	15.00-20.00
	"HOT FOOT" ASHTRAY	25.00-35.00
	"LITTLE SIDE KICK" ASHTRAY	20.00-25.00
87	NUBIAN BUST ASHTRAY	50.00-55.00
	COCONUT MUGS, Each	5.00-10.00
	BANANA LEAF ASHTRAY	10.00-15.00
	CIGARETTE RESTS, Each	10.00-15.00
	SEA MYTH ASHTRAYS, Each	15.00-20.00
88	WOODLAND ASH BOWL	10.00-15.00
	SHELL CANDLEHOLDERS, Each	15.00-20.00
	HORN O'PLENTY	35.00-45.00
	COUCH SHELL BOWLS, Each	25.00-35.00
89	TUMBLER	20.00-25.00
	PEDESTAL VASE	20.00-25.00
	CABBAGE LEAF FOOTED BOWL	35.00-50.00
	SPORTSMAN'S DUCK PLATTER	45.00-55.00
90	COWBOY HAT MINT TRAY/ ASHTRAY	35.00-45.00
	COWBOY HAT HORS d'OEUVRE TRAY	45.00-55.00
	FIDDLE LEAF BOWL	15.00-20.00
	CACHE POT	25.00-30.00
91	CABBAGE LEAF COMPOTE	15.00-20.00
	FLOWER BOWLS, Each	25.00-35.00
	URN	25.00-30.00
	FOOTED FLOWER BOWL	12.00-15.00
92	SHELL FAN BOWL	15.00-20.00
	ADVANCE DESIGN BOWLS, Each	10.00-15.00
	GARDEN CLUB DISH	20.00-25.00

WINART POTTERY

94	DECANTER	30.00-40.00
95	TWO TIER TRAY	25.00-30.00
	HORSE-SHOES, Each	5.00-10.00
96	LAZY-SUSAN	30.00-35.00
	CHIP 'N DIP PLATE	15.00-20.00
	BOWL, 24. OZ.	5.00-10.00
97	PITCHER 6"	5.00-10.00
	PITCHER 2 1/2 QT.	15.00-20.00
	JUICE TUMBLER W/ CAROUSEL TRAY	30.00-35.00
	JUICE TUMBLER	4.00-7.00
	JUICE PITCHER	25.00-30.00
98	PITCHER	10.00-15.00
	COFFEE SERVER	85.00-100.00
	PITCHER 2 1/2 QT.	15.00-20.00
	INDIVIDUAL TEAPOT	15.00-20.00
99	TEAPOT 48 OZ.	65.00-75.00
	TEAPOT 28 OZ.	65.00-75.00
	COFFEE SERVER	85.00-100.00
	MUGS W/CAROUSEL TRAY	25.00-35.00
100	MUGS W/CAROUSEL TRAY	15.00-20.00
	MUG	3.00-6.00
	TEAPOT 12-CUP	60.00-70.00
	SIP 'N SMOKE TRAY	10.00-15.00
	TWO FINGER MUG	5.00-8.00
101	BOWL 48 OZ.	8.00-12.00
	10" BAKER/BOWL	10.00-15.00
	BOWL 2 QT.	10.00-20.00
	AU GRATIN DISH	10.00-15.00
	PEDESTAL MUG	8.00-12.00
	MUG	3.00-6.00
	7" PLATE/SAUCER	3.00-5.00
	10" PLATE	7.00-10.00
	DESSERT BOWL	4.00-6.00
	SALAD/SOUP BOWL	6.00-8.00
102	FREE FORM BOWLS, Each	15.00-20.00
	SALAD/PUNCH BOWL	40.00-50.00
	THREE-GALLON BOWL	50.00-60.00
103	THREE-LEG CASSEROLE	12.00-20.00
	PITCHER	10.00-15.00
	CREAMER, Each	5.00-10.00
	SUGAR	5.00-8.00
	PITCHER	5.00-10.00
	SALT & PEPPER (Ball)	8.00-15.00
	SALT & PEPPER	14.00-20.00
104	SCALLOPED INDIVIDUAL DISH	5.00-10.00
	TOOTHPICK/MATCH HOLDER	4.00-8.00
	ROUND INDIVIDUAL DISH	4.00-8.00
	BUTTER DISH	10.00-15.00
	RELISH DISH	10.00-15.00
	WAGON WHEEL LAZY-SUSAN	35.00-45.00
	WAGON WHEEL LAZY-SUSAN W/STAND & COFFEE SERVICE	75.00-100.00
105	MIAMI ASHTRAY	8.00-12.00
	WIND PROOF ASHTRAY	8.00-12.00
	FREE FORM ASHTRAY	15.00-20.00
	CIGARETTE LIGHTER	8.00-15.00
	DRAFT PROOF ASHTRAY	10.00-15.00
106	MUG W/CHRISTMAS SCENE	5.00-10.00
	PEDESTAL MUG W/ CHRISTMAS SCENE	10.00-15.00
	PLANTER	10.00-20.00

	PLANTER	10.00-20.00
	OBLONG PLANTER	25.00-35.00
107	WALL MASK	30.00-40.00

SEQUOYAH POTTERY

109	SEQUOYAH'S HOME	40.00-65.00
110	KNEELING POTTERS, Each	75.00-95.00
	FROG	40-00 50.00
	LARGE KNEELING POTTER	125.00-150.00
111	ASHTRAY	40.00-50.00
	TURTLE ASHTRAY	45.00-55.00
	VASE	65.00-75.00
	VASE	100.00-125.00
112	FROG PLANTER	85.00-115.00
	DUCK PLANTER	75.00-95.00
	INDIAN POT	30.00-35.00
	BOWL	45.00-50.00
113	PLANTER	85.00-115.00
	FROG HANDLE VASE	90.00-120.00
	PLANTER	65.00-75.00
	VASE	50.00-65.00
114	PLANTER	65.00-75.00
	OWL NECK PLANTER	80.00-95.00
	URN	175.00-200.00
115	THUNDERBIRD PITCHERS, Each	30.00-35.00
	VASE	85.00-100.00
	STRAIGHT NECK VASE	45.00-55.00
116	FROG HANDLE PITCHERS, Each	75.00-100.00
117	FROG HANDLE PITCHERS, Each	75.00-100.00
	VASE	75.00-85.00
	PLANTER	75.00-85.00
118	DOG VASE	300.00-350.00
	DUCK ASHTRAY	95.00-115.00
	VASE	65.00-75.00
	PITCHER	45.00-55.00

NYA POTTERY

119	BOTTLE VASES, Each	25.00-40.00
120	BOTTLE VASES, Each	25.00-40.00
	PITCHER 20 OZ.	25.00-35.00

	PITCHER 3 QT.	55.00-75.00
	BOTTLE PITCHER	30.00-40.00
	SALT & PEPPER	15.00-20.00

SYNAR CERAMICS

121	ASHTRAY	15.00-20.00
122	CANNIBAL	25.00-30.00
	PINE CONE VASE	15.00-20.00
	CORK BARK BOWL	15.00-20.00
	WHEAT VASE	15.00-20.00
123	PLANTER	8.00-12.00
	ROUND PLANTER	8.00-12.00
	SQUARE FOOTED VASE	15.00-20.00
	HANDLED VASE W/STICKER	25.00-30.00
	BASKET	15.00-20.00
124	DEEP BOWL	15.00-20.00
	SHALLOW BOWL	12.00-15.00
	WALL POCKET	20.00-25.00
125	SYNAR CHRISTMAS CARD	40.00-50.00
	LOTUS BOWL	5.00-10.00
	OVAL PLANTER	8.00-12.00
	BOWL	25.00-30.00

GRACETONE POTTERY

126	LARGE ENGLISH SETTER	175.00-200.00
	LARGE TERRIER	185.00-215.00
	HOUND DOG	300.00-350.00
127	GRACETONE CHRISTMAS CARDS, Each	75.00-85.00
	TALL VASE	25.00-30.00
	GLAD VASE	30.00-35.00
	BOTTLE VASE	25.00-35.00
	PEDESTALLED BOWL	20.00-25.00
128	SUGAR W/LID	15.00-20.00
	SALT & PEPPER	15.00-20.00
	CREAMER	12.00-15.00
	CUP	6.00-10.00
	SAUCER	2.00-3.00
	PLATE 10"	8.00-12.00
	PLATE 7"	5.00-7.00
	FRUIT BOWL	4.00-7.00
	SCALLOPED BOWL	8.00-12.00
	ROUND PLANTER	8.00-12.00

129	PITCHER	40.00-45.00
	WARMER	15.00-20.00
	ASHTRAY	30.00-35.00
	ASHTRAY	15.00-20.00

CREEK POTTERY

130	HORSE	5.00-10.00
	LARGE MALLARD	15.00-20.00
	SMALL MALLARD	8.00-10.00
131	VASE	10.00-15.00
	TEPEE SALT & PEPPER	8.00-12.00
	DUCK EGG CUP	5.00-8.00
132	OWL FIGURINE/BOOK END	8.00-12.00
	INDIAN HEAD MUG	5.00-10.00
	PLANTER	5.00-10.00
	BUFFALO NICKEL BANK	15.00-20.00
	MOCCASIN	5.00-10.00

CHEROKEE POTTERY

133	QUAIL	5.00-10.00
	INDIAN HEAD BUST	25.00-30.00
	INDIAN BOWL	20.00-25.00
134	HORSE	10.00-15.00
	BUNNIES, Pair	10.00-15.00
	BUFFALO	15.00-20.00
135	PLATE	5.00-8.00
	BOWL 9"	5.00-10.00
	BOWL 10 OZ.	3.00-4.00
	CUP	3.00-4.00
	BOTTLE	8.00-12.00
	"HONEY" BEAR	15.00-20.00

OTHER OKLAHOMA ARTIST

136	GNOME	225.00-250.00
	POLYNESIAN WOMAN	150.00-200.00
	INDIAN PLAQUE	125.00-150.00
137	VASE	25.00-35.00
	PLATE	10.00-15.00
	BOWL	25.00-35.00
	VASE	25.00-35.00

Index